HORSELESS CARRIAGE
The Motor-Car in England

By the same author

NARROW BOAT
HIGH HORSE RIDERLESS
SLEEP NO MORE
WORCESTERSHIRE
GREEN AND SILVER
THE INLAND WATERWAYS OF ENGLAND

The first " Silver Ghost " Rolls Royce of 1907. *Photographed* 1950.

FRONTISPIECE

L. T. C. ROLT

Horseless Carriage

The Motor-Car in England

CONSTABLE · PUBLISHERS · LONDON

LONDON
PUBLISHED BY
Constable and Company Ltd
10–12 ORANGE STREET, W.C.2

·

INDIA AND PAKISTAN
Orient Longmans Ltd
BOMBAY   CALCUTTA   MADRAS

·

CANADA
Longmans, Green and Company
TORONTO

·

SOUTH *and* EAST AFRICA
Longmans, Green and Company Ltd
CAPE TOWN   NAIROBI

First published 1950

PRINTED IN GREAT BRITAIN BY W. & J. MACKAY & CO., LTD., CHATHAM

INTRODUCTION AND
ACKNOWLEDGEMENTS

FOR CENTURIES the English road, aided to a limited extent by the navigable river, provided the only means of inland communication. Then came the canal era. The canal boat superseded the pack-horse and the wagon but the road still flourished, for the canal age was also the heyday of the stage-coach when the great posting-houses grew up along the trunk routes. But the supremacy of the canal boat and the stage coach was short lived. The railway came to challenge both ; the high road echoed no more the thunder of hooves or the triumphant cry of the coachman's horn ; grass grew between the cobbles of the inn court-yards and the " Railway Hotels " flourished in their stead. The steam coach tried in vain to break the railway monopoly and it was not until the close of the nineteenth century that the strength of a new power—the internal combustion engine—proved irresistible and brought the road into its own again.

This third revolution in the history of land transport has had far more profound social and economic consequences than either of its predecessors. Moreover, whereas both the canal and the railway systems quickly reached a definitive stage of development, the revolution wrought by the in-ternal combustion engine is still proceeding so that its ultimate results are more difficult to assess.

Any book which aimed to give a complete and detailed history of the road revolution in England would necessarily be a weighty, and possibly exhaustive tome. This book has been written with the more modest aim of providing for the general reader a broad outline of the evolution in England of one class of vehicle—the private motor-car. Yet even so, the field is wide, for although the engine of the modern car has a comparatively brief history, its chassis and transmission have a much older lineage. A feature such as the differential gear, for example, represents the solution of a knotty technical problem which was first found by the long forgotten builders of steam road carriages. Hence it is in this period that the beginning of the story must be set.

Our canal and railway systems were exclusively national achievements owing little or nothing to overseas influence or example. In fact it is well known that England was the pioneer of the railway age. But the locomotive and the steamship between them broke down the natural barriers between nations and brought about a much freer and more rapid interchange of ideas. As a consequence, although this is primarily a study of the evolution of the English car, Continental, and even transatlantic developments cannot be wholly ignored because of their influence upon English design. Continental influence was particularly strong in the early days of the " horseless carriage " owing to the legal handicap which crippled English designers, while in the '20s transatlantic practice was responsible for the introduction of mass-production methods. Again, it is quite impossible to consider motor racing from an exclusively national standpoint since the sport has always represented an international pool of advanced design from which the English production car has drawn benefit.

I have deliberately avoided entering into too much technical detail which would be intelligible only to the motor engineer. Nevertheless, in a work of this nature it is impossible to avoid the use of a certain amount of technical phraseology and I hope I may be forgiven if, in my attempt to reach a happy compromise in this respect, my writing strikes the layman as too technical or the expert as too elementary.

Finally I would like to acknowledge with gratitude the unstinting help I have received from many friends in the motoring world, notably Messrs. Cecil Clutton, Anthony Heal and David Curwen, whose technical and historical knowledge of the subject is much more intimate than mine. I would also like to thank for their willing help all those who provided photographs for illustration, particularly the Editor and Staff of *The Autocar* and Mr. R. B. Winyard of the Veteran Car Club. In addition I must record my indebtedness to the authors of the works mentioned in the short bibliography which appears at the end of this book.

L.T.C.R.

CONTENTS

ILLUSTRATIONS

ILLUSTRATIONS

CHAPTER ONE

EARLY PRIMITIVES

Soon shall thy arm, unconquered steam, afar
Drag the slow barge, or drive the rapid car . . .

ERASMUS DARWIN

IT IS THE spring of the year 1766 in the Midlands of
England. The hedgerows are still bare but the meadows
are freshly green and purple buds have blurred the
black filigree of the elms. In 200 years the scene has
changed scarcely at all except that the quickset hedges of
enclosure are beginning to alter the pattern of the fields.
The primitive coal workings have as yet hardly marked the
folds of Cannock Chase and from their slopes of heather
and bracken the green levels of the valleys of Trent and
Tame spread away to the east, no chimneys, no smudges of
smoke, but only the triple spires of Lichfield pricking the
wide spring skies above them. Those skies are filled with
the music of larks soaring invisible in the sunshine, for it is
very quiet. No Trent Valley line with its thunderous Scotch
expresses skirts the Chase, and the Roman Ryknield Street
is not yet reborn as a tarmac highway roaring with motor
traffic.

With a clatter of hooves and a rumble of wheels a closed
carriage comes swaying and jolting down the rough track
that leads towards the distant town, a water pail and a
bundle of fodder swinging from the boot. The solitary,
soberly clad occupant of the carriage is engaged in exploring

13

the contents of a large hamper filled with fruit and other comestibles, but because the cramped interior is piled to the windows with books it is not easy to see him at all from the roadside. This is a doctor from Lichfield returning from his rounds and his name is Erasmus Darwin.

Member of the celebrated Lunar Society, physician, scientist, poet and bibliophile, Doctor Darwin was a typical member of an intellectual circle which seems to us, in our age of specialisation, remarkable for its catholicity. The sum of human knowledge and the accumulated fund of experience was not then so vast that a brilliant intellect could not comprehend the whole pattern and even master a considerable portion of it. Such mastery induced a feeling of self-confident optimism which left the mind free to speculate and was thus responsible for that extraordinary fertility in invention which characterised the last decades of the eighteenth century. For the first time men began to realise the immense potentiality of applied science. The newly discovered power of steam alone seemed to the eighteenth century philosopher to herald a Golden Age, and it never occurred to him to doubt the capacity of human nature to control the powers conferred upon it. We who have discovered in sorrow and bewilderment that the tree of knowledge bears bitter fruit may be pardoned if we envy these forefathers their unclouded optimism.

As his carriage bore him slowly through the Staffordshire lanes, Doctor Darwin pondered the possibility of applying steam power to road vehicles, and on the evening following our imaginary encounter we may picture him ensconced at his desk in his candlelit study in Lichfield. He is writing a letter to his friend Matthew Boulton in Birmingham and as we read his eager sentences we seem to hear the squeaking

14

and scratching of his furious quill and to see the fire settling
unheeded, the candles guttering unsnuffed.

" As I was riding home yesterday," he writes, " I considered the scheme of the fiery chariot, and the longer I
contemplated this favourite idea, the more practicable it
appeared to me.

" I shall lay my thoughts before you, crude and undi-
gested as they appeared to me, and by these hints you may
be led into various trains of thinking upon this subject,
and by that means (if any hints can assist your genius,
which, without hints, is above all others I am acquainted
with) be more likely to approve or disapprove. And as I
am quite mad of the scheme, I hope you will not show this
paper to anyone. These things are required : (1) a rotary
motion ; (2) easily altering its direction ; (3) to be
accelerated, retarded, destroyed, revived instantly and
easily ; (4) the bulk, the weight, the expense of the machine
to be as small as possible in proportion to its power."

Today, Darwin's four requirements appear to be merely
a statement of the obvious, but at that time, when the
mechanically propelled road vehicle was still no more than
an embryo in the womb of the mechanical mind, it was an
admirably lucid statement of first principles which remains
as true today as it was when it was written. When we assess
the merits of a modern motor-car we still apply Doctor
Darwin's standards, and not infrequently find it wanting
because manufacturers, even today, fail especially to appreciate the importance of keeping " the bulk, the weight as
small as possible."

It is one thing to enunciate theoretical principles, however admirable, but it is a far more difficult matter to translate them into practice. The crude drawings and specification of a steam carriage on the Newcomen atmospheric
principle which Darwin sent to Boulton could never have

taken practical shape, and the credit for producing the first full-size mechanical vehicle actually to run on the road must be conceded to the Frenchman Nicholas Joseph Cugnot of Void in Lorraine. As early as 1763 he is said to have exhibited a model steam carriage, and in 1769 his first full-size carriage was tested on the road. On its first run it carried four persons at $2\frac{1}{4}$ m.p.h. but, like so many later steam vehicles, the steaming capacity of the boiler was inadequate with the result that after twenty minutes' running the vehicle had to stand for a further twenty minutes to regain steam pressure. The boiler feed pumps were also very defective. Nothing daunted, Cugnot constructed a second, larger and improved carriage to the order of the Minister of War for the purpose of drawing cannon. A two-cylinder, single-acting, high-pressure engine drove the single front wheel by an ingenious system of pawls, the action of which could be reversed to allow the vehicle to run backwards. The machine ran well, but unfortunately, with its internally fired copper boiler overhanging the front wheel, weight distribution could scarcely have been worse, and in consequence it signally failed to fulfil Doctor Darwin's second principle. Cugnot's first vehicle had distinguished itself by knocking down a stone wall, and his second overturned in a spectacular fashion when attempting to turn a street corner near the church of the Madeleine in Paris. In consequence both the machine and its unfortunate inventor were imprisoned to keep them out of further mischief. Thus Cugnot, fifty years ahead of his time, suffered the fate which attends all such pioneers.

That thirty years were to pass before Cugnot's achievement was equalled, let alone surpassed, in England was in a great measure due to the intolerant and arrogant attitude of James Watt. No one can belittle the magnitude of Watt's achievement ; the magnificent steam engines which were the product of his fruitful partnership with Matthew Boulton bear the hall-mark of inventive genius of the first order. Nor can it be doubted that, from the commercial point of view, the famous partners were right in concentrating all their energies on the development of the stationary steam engine rather than embarking upon fresh enterprises of so highly speculative a nature as the application of the new power to road vehicles. But his long struggle to secure the recognition of his invention and the reward which was his due had made Watt an embittered, suspicious and jealous man. Even his ultimate success and public acclaim did little to mellow his uncompromising temperament. In his estimation, what he did not know about the new power was not worth knowing, and he refused to believe that anyone else was capable of improving the steam engine or of adapting it to new purposes. If he would not or could not build a steam carriage, then he was sure that no one else could, and he did his utmost to discourage any inventor who dared to challenge his monopoly. In 1769 Watt's friend Doctor Small, who had repeatedly urged him to consider the problem of the steam carriage, wrote to him as follows : " A linen draper at London, one Moore, has taken out a patent for moving wheel carriages by steam. This comes of thy delays. I daresay he has heard of your inventions." To this Watt replied truculently : " if linen draper Moore does not use my engine to drive his chaises, he cannot drive them by steam. If he does I will stop him. I suppose by the rapidity of his progress and puffing, he is too volatile to be dangerous." Nothing further was heard of Moore.

Watt adopted a similar attitude to the speculations of Lovell Edgeworth and to the work of William Symington the brilliant Scotch engineer who, besides being responsible for the first successful steam boat, *Charlotte Dundas*, constructed a model steam carriage. We may therefore well imagine the great man's reaction on hearing the news that William Murdoch, Boulton & Watt's chief assistant, had constructed a model steam carriage while working for the firm in Cornwall. The little model ran well and its first test in 1784, in a dark tree-lined avenue leading to the church at Redruth, has been remembered where many similar trials have been forgotten because the vicar encountered the carriage, which had outpaced its inventor, and fled in terror in the belief that he was being assailed by the Evil One in person. Murdoch was sternly advised to give up his experiments and concentrate in future on the firm's business.

As an example of the lengths to which Watt carried his prejudice, he actually inserted a clause in the lease of his house at Heathfield, Birmingham, to the effect that "no steam carriage should on any pretence be allowed to approach the house." Nevertheless, Watt did himself take out a steam-carriage patent in 1784, although it would seem that this move was merely a show of force calculated to discourage and circumvent others, for he never made any attempt to translate the patent into practice. It was just as well for Watt's reputation that he did not do so, for the design, with its low-pressure wooden boiler and air condenser cooled by bellows was foredoomed to failure. The only good feature of the specification was the transmission which was highly ingenious. The engine was to drive a countershaft connected to the axle by gearing. Three gear wheels of different sizes were to be locked on the countershaft and engaged with three pinions which, in the neutral position, floated on the axle. By means of a sliding key connected to the change-speed control each driven pinion could be individually locked on the axle. This, in effect, was a three-speed, constant-mesh gearbox, almost certainly the first ever evolved.

The success of Cugnot's carriage had undoubtedly been due to his use of high-pressure steam. Although Watt was well aware of the expansive power of high-pressure steam, throughout his long life he refused to believe that the application of the principle was a practical engineering proposition. Instead he pinned his faith in the low-pressure condensing engine which, though suitable for stationary or marine purposes, was too heavy and cumbersome to be successful on a road vehicle. Because his influence on engineering thought in eighteenth-century England was very great, this prejudice of Watt's undoubtedly retarded the birth of the successful steam carriage.

The man who was eventually responsible for that birth was the Cornishman, Richard Trevithick of Illogan. Trevithick was an inventive genius equally as great as James Watt, and that his name, though widely known today, has never achieved the same popular renown is due to the fact that he never enjoyed worldly success or recognition in his lifetime. Like so many pioneers before and after him, Trevithick died impoverished ; he was only saved from a pauper's grave by a subscription raised by his workmates at John Hall's factory at Dartford.

Trevithick has justly been described as the father of the high-pressure engine, and his commercial failure was due to the chronic lack of funds from which he always suffered. History shows that the inventor only succeeds in his lifetime if he is fortunate enough to find a partner of wealth, influence, courage and foresight. Such men are as rare as inventors, and for poor Trevithick there was no Matthew Boulton or Edward Pease. How far ahead of his time

Trevithick was is revealed by the description of his first road vehicle. It had a cast-iron cylindrical boiler with an internal return fire tube. It was fitted with a spring safety valve set to lift at 60 lb. pressure, and a fusible plug in the crown of the fire-flue. The single vertical cylinder was mounted in the boiler and the piston rod drove the wheels via a crosshead and two connecting rods attached to crank-pins. The valve motion and a boiler feed pump were driven off the crosshead, and the steam exhausted through a blast nozzle in the chimney after heating the feed water.

Trevithick began to build this vehicle in Tyack's work-shop at Camborne in November, 1800, the equipment available consisting of two smith's hearths and a small hand-lathe. The castings were made at Harvey's famous foundry at Hale, some of the turning work was done at Captain Andrew Vivian's workshop, while parts of the boiler and other details came from the Shropshire foundries of Coalbrookdale. In 1858, an old man still living in Camborne gave the following fascinating eye-witness account of Trevithick's first trial, the first journey ever made by a mechanical road vehicle on the roads of England.

"I knew Captain Dick Trevithick very well. I was a cooper by trade, and when Trevithick was making his steam carriage I used to go every day into John Tyack's shop at the Weigh, close by here, where they put her together. In the year 1801, upon Christmas Eve, towards night, Trevithick got up steam, out on the high road, just outside the shop. When we saw that Trevithick was going to turn on steam, we jumped up as many as could, maybe seven or eight of us. 'Twas a stiffish hill going up to Camborne Beacon, but she went off like a little bird. When she had gone about a quarter of a mile, there was a rough piece of road, covered with loose stones. She didn't go quite so fast, and it was a flood of rain, and as we were very much squeezed together, I jumped off. She was going faster than I could walk, and went up the hill about half a mile further, when they turned her, and came back again to the shop."

But alas, after so promising a start Trevithick's little steamer came to an untimely end only a few days later. Trevithick's friend Davies Giddy recounts the sad story as follows :

" The Travelling Engine took its departure from Camborne Church Town for Tehidy on the 28th of Decr, 1801, where I was waiting to receive it. The carriage, however, broke down after travelling very well, and up an ascent, in all about three or four hundred yards. The carriage was forced under some shelter, and the Parties adjourned to the Hotel, & comforted their Hearts with a Roast Goose & proper drinks, when, forgetful of the Engine, its Water boiled away, the Iron became red hot, and nothing that was combustible remained either of the Engine or the house."

Both the failure to remember the boiler fire and Giddy's phraseology suggest that the alcohol consumed was of a potency and quantity proper to the Festive Season, and the unfortunate inventor had reason bitterly to regret the timing of his experiment.

Nevertheless, despite its brief career the promise of this first road carriage was sufficient to encourage Trevithick and Vivian to become partners, to travel to London and there to take out a steam-carriage patent in the following March. It was in accordance with this specification that Trevithick constructed his London Steam Carriage in 1803. This was of entirely different design and incorporated many improvements. The cylindrical boiler was mounted at the back and fired from a rear platform. The single cylinder was set horizontally in the boiler, protruding through the front cover plate. The piston drove a cranked countershaft by means of a piston rod which was forked to clear the crank and connecting rod, a novel device which made the machinery more compact. Small wheels had made the first vehicle very unstable and had not proved suitable for the rough roads of the period. To overcome this defect the new steamer was equipped with an enormous pair of wooden driving wheels 10 ft. in diameter which were connected by gearing to the crankshaft. The vehicle was steered by means of a single front wheel and a towering coach body seating eight to ten persons was perched on springs above the machinery. To contemporary eyes the result must have been impressive indeed.

This formidable equipage was constructed at Felton's carriage shop in Leather Lane, but the machinery was made and tested at Harvey's foundry at Hale and dispatched to London by sea. When it was completed the carriage made a number of successful trips through the streets of London and it is most remarkable that events so unprecedented appear to have excited no comment in the press of the day. Partly, no doubt, because of the saving in weight which had been effected, the carriage steamed better than its predecessor and on one occasion it made a journey of 10 miles, travelling from Leather Lane to Gray's Inn Lane, Lord's Cricket Ground, Paddington, Islington and back. On another occasion it passed down Oxford Street at a fast speed to the accompaniment of much cheering, all horse traffic having been cleared from the roadway.

Once again there has fortunately survived a first-hand account of one of these historical runs with the first horseless carriage ever to appear on the streets of London. As a rule Trevithick looked after the firing and the engine controls while Andrew Vivian steered, but on one occasion the latter's son John, then aged nineteen was allowed to take the tiller. Sixty-five years later John Vivian recalled this experience as follows :

" One day they started about four o'clock in the morning, and went along Tottenham Court Road, and the New Road or City Road : there was a canal by the side of the road at one place, for he was thinking how deep it was if they should run into it. They kept going on for four or five miles, and sometimes at the rate of eight or nine miles an hour. I was steering, and Captain Trevithick and someone else were attending to the engine. Captain Dick came alongside of me and said, ' She is going all right.' ' Yes,' I said, ' I think we had better go on to Cornwall.' She was going along five or six miles an hour, and Captain Dick called out, ' Put the helm down, John ! ' and before I could tell what was up, Captain Dick's foot was upon the steering-wheel handle, and we were tearing down six or seven yards of railing from a garden wall. A person put his head from a window, and called out, ' What the devil are you doing there ! What the devil is that thing ? '

" They got her back to the coach factory. A great cause of difficulty was the fire-bars shaking loose, and letting the fire fall through into the ash-pan.

" The waste steam was turned into the chimney and, puffed out with the smoke at each stroke of the engine. When the steam was up, she went capitally well, but when the fire-bars dropped, and the fire got out of order, she did not go well."

These two steam vehicles of Trevithick's, so very different in their design might be said to represent the sources of two distinct streams of mechanical evolution which were destined to diverge more widely as the years went by. The first experiment produced what was in essence a road locomotive, the railless equivalent of the inventor's famous " Catch-me-who-can." It might therefore be called the ancestor of the steam traction engine, initiating a course of development which does not concern us here. The London Steamer, on the other hand, was unquestionably a " horseless carriage " and so has a strong claim to be called the first progenitor of the modern English motor-car.

It might be supposed that the success of Trevithick's experiments would have been followed by rapid development, but this was not the case. Owing to financial difficulties, Trevithick made no further experiments, while there was no technical press in those days to disseminate news of mechanical inventions. In consequence, blind to what Trevithick had already achieved, many ingenious mechanics continued to evolve the most wildly impracticable schemes for road vehicles. Thus William Brunton and David Gordon refused to believe that smooth-tyred wheels could possibly propel a vehicle. Both actually built steam carriages which were propelled by mechanical feet. Moreover, the carriages ran, albeit slowly, the systems of levers by which the feet were actuated by the piston rods being marvels of misapplied ingenuity. Another inventor had the happy notion of supplementing steam-power by a windmill driven partly by the wind and partly by the exhaust steam. John Dumbell, in 1808, went further and suggested doing away with a reciprocating engine and driving his carriage by causing the steam to play " upon a series of vanes or fliers acting within a cylinder." This idea, impracticable though it proved at the time, contains the germ of the invention of the turbine.

It would not be appropriate to describe all the carriages which were built in the nineteenth century, but only to mention those which were outstandingly successful or which included mechanical features which were later to appear in the twentieth century motor-car.

It is unfortunate that few details seem to have survived

of the road vehicle patented and constructed in 1823 by Samuel Brown which was driven by " a patent gas vacuum engine." The motive power of this engine was the vacuum produced by the combustion of a mixture of carburetted hydrogen and air in a vessel separate from the cylinder and connected with it by valve gear of steam-engine type. The carriage is said to have ascended Shooter's Hill to the satisfaction of a large crowd of spectators, and a Canal Gas Engine Company was formed with the idea of using the engine to propel canal boats. The company was soon dissolved because, it is said, the engine proved very costly to run.

Another unsuccessful attempt to utilise a motive power other than steam was the compressed air carriage. As early as 1799 William Medhurst patented " an improved Aeolian engine " with which he proposed to drive carriages. He advocated a system of air driven stage-coaches throughout the country and the construction of compressor stations at suitable points along the roads. Medhurst's ideas were subsequently taken up by other inventors, notably Samuel Wright (1828), William Mann of Brixton (1829) and Von Rathen. Wright and Von Rathen are said to have actually constructed air-driven carriages in 1832 and 1848 respectively, the latter being tested on the road at Putney.

In 1824, T. Burstall of Edinburgh and J. Hill of London patented and built a steam coach which exhibited many original features. The boiler was described as a " heat generator " the water being kept in a separate vessel and fed into the boiler in a quantity proportionate to the demand for steam. The water so admitted was instantly vaporised by falling on a series of heated metal trays. This, of course, was the principle of the flash boiler which was re-introduced in the steam car of modern times. The carriage had the further distinction of being the first vehicle fitted with four-wheel drive. The power of the two-cylinder engine was applied directly to cranks on the rear axle, and the drive to the front wheels was provided by a bevel gear between the crank throws which engaged a propeller shaft of familiar pattern. At the front end, the propeller shaft bevel meshed with an intermediate horizontal crown wheel on the axis of the pivoting axle so that the front wheel drive did not interfere with the steering. The mechanical problem created by the fact that one driving wheel had to travel further than its neighbour on corners was already exercising the ingenuity of inventors. Some shirked it by driving on one wheel only, but Burstall & Hill used a system of ratchet wheels and pawls in each wheel hub which included a locking device to enable the carriage to move in reverse. Later, the inventors discarded the ratchets in favour of clutches, but the vehicle never performed satisfactorily because the patent boiler proved a failure.

W. H. James of Thavies Inn, Holborn, was responsible at the same period for an equally ingenious and more successful carriage. The heart of the steam carriage was the boiler, and James had patented a very satisfactory tubular boiler which worked at 200 lb. pressure, a remarkably high pressure for the time. James tackled the cornering problem by employing two small and light two-cylinder engines to drive each of the two driving wheels, the steam admission valves being interconnected with the steering gear so that, to use marine parlance, when the tiller was turned to port, more steam was admitted to the starboard engine while the port engine was throttled down and vice versa. This arrangement must surely have satisfied Doctor Darwin's second requirement of " easily altered direction," only too well, in fact the effect of a full-lock turn must have been more than a little startling for all concerned. James evidently recognised the importance of keeping down unsprung weight, for the whole of the mechanism was sprung, and to avoid the possibility of fracture owing to vibration and relative movement, the steam supply to the engines was taken through the tubular frame members which supported the cylinders. One of James's carriages travelled through Epping Forest at a speed of 12 to 15 m.p.h. with fifteen passengers on board.

Much more remarkable was the performance achieved by the two high-speed carriages constructed by Messrs. Summers & Ogle in 1831. The first carriage had a two- and the second a three-cylinder engine, while the boiler in each case was of vertical type, coke-fired, with forced draught by engine driven fan, and with a working pressure of 250 lb. On its initial trial, the first carriage ran from London to within 2½ miles of Basingstoke where the crankshaft broke, the return journey being made ignominiously by barge on the Basingstoke canal. The second carriage made a number of long journeys at remarkable speed, its best performance being a run from Southampton turnpike gate to the four-mile stone on the London road at an average of 24½ m.p.h., with a full load, the maximum being 32 m.p.h. When we bear in mind the roads of the period, the solid wheels and the crude springing and steering, this achievement is at once scarcely credible and terrifying to contemplate.

By this time the steam road vehicle had left the purely experimental stage and might have been introduced widely had it not been for the bitter opposition of the horse coach industry. Hitherto they had tolerated the mechanical road vehicle as an impracticable toy, but now they began to realise that it was a dangerous competitor. For four months in 1831 Sir Charles Dance ran a regular service between Gloucester and Cheltenham with steam coaches built by Sir Goldsworthy Gurney, carrying 3,000 passengers a distance of 4,000 miles. Heaps of loose stones were eventually laid across the road to prevent the coaches from running. Similar tactics in Scotland prevented John Scott Russell's coaches from running between Glasgow and Paisley in 1834.

Most successful of all the steam coach builders of the period was Walter Hancock of Stratford, London, who built altogether ten vehicles which included the *Infant* (with oscillating cylinders) the *Era*, *Enterprise*, *Erin*, *Autopsy* and *Automaton* which were operated by the London & Paddington Omnibus Company on a regular service between these places. The venture was not a commercial success, however, and Hancock was badly served by the Company.

Another builder of steam vehicles who deserves to be better known was Colonel Francis Maceroni, the son of an Italian born Manchester merchant. With their vertical multitubular boilers with fan induced draught, Maceroni's carriages somewhat resembled those made by Summers & Ogle, and like the latter they showed a remarkable turn of speed. For a time, one of them ran regularly between Paddington and Edgware. An account of a trip on one of Maceroni's vehicles which appeared in *Turner's Annual Tour* in 1834 is worth quoting as it presents an entertaining picture of road travel at that time :

" Drawn out of a hut on Bushy Heath by the appearance of an unusual commotion amongst the inhabitants of the village, we saw a steam coach which stopped there. The apparition of a vehicle of this kind, in such a place, was

unaccountable. Bushy Heath forms the plateau of a mountain, which is the highest point of land in Middlesex, and,
although far inland, serves as a landmark for vessels at sea.
The access to it, from the London side, is by a difficult and
steep road. Being accosted by Colonel Maceroni, in whom
we were glad to recognise an old acquaintance, he informed
us that the journey had been performed with ease, adding
that it was his intention to proceed to Watford.

" Now if the road from Edgware to Bushy Heath was
steep and difficult, the descent from Bushy Heath to Watford was much worse. We told our friend that he might go
by steam to Watford, but that we were quite certain that
he would not return by the same means of locomotion.
Nevertheless, at his pressing instance, we consented to
hazard our own person in the adventure. We set off,
amidst the cheers of the villagers. The motion was so
steady that we could have read with ease, and the noise was
no worse than that produced by a common vehicle. On
arriving at the summit of Clay Hill, the local and inexperienced attendant neglected to clog the wheel until it
became impossible. We went thundering down the hill at
the rate of thirty miles an hour. Mr. Squire was steersman,
and never lost his presence of mind. It may be conceived
what amazement a thing of this kind, flashing through the
village of Bushy, occasioned among the inhabitants. The
people seemed petrified on seeing a carriage without horses.
In the busy and populous town of Watford the sensation
was similar—the men gazed in speechless wonder ; the
women clapped their hands. We turned round at the end
of the street in magnificent style, and ascended Clay Hill
at the same rate as the stage coaches drawn by five horses,
and at length regained our starting place."

In 1833, a steam carriage constructed by Mr. Roberts of
the firm of Sharp, Roberts & Co., of Manchester made its
first trial trip. Its performance was not particularly remarkable ; in fact on one occasion when it was travelling through
the streets of Manchester a boiler tube burst, scattering coke

in all directions and breaking several shop windows. Nevertheless, this carriage represented another very important milestone in the technical evolution of the motor-car, for Roberts had solved the final drive problem by evolving what was then called a " compensating gear." This was no less than the differential gear, a device of great ingenuity which was soon destined to supersede the ratchets and clutches which had hitherto prevailed, and to be universally applied to all road vehicles from traction engines to light cars. In after years, others were to claim credit for inventing the gear, notably a certain Mr. Schmidt who took out a patent for the device as late as 1868, but there can be little doubt that the credit is due to Roberts who, like Trevithick, died in poverty.

Among those who were quick to adopt Roberts's gear was F. Hill of Dartford who constructed some very successful carriages in 1840 and 1841. While many vehicle builders cautiously confined their trials to the neighbourhood of London, Hill ranged far afield to Windsor, Brighton, Hastings, Bromley and Tunbridge. On one occasion he ran from London to Hastings and back in the day, a round trip of 128 miles, at twice the speed of the stage coaches.

The success of these road steamers led to the promotion of a scheme for a special steam-carriageway from London to Holyhead, no less a person than Thomas Telford being named as engineer. Wheel ways of rectangular stone blocks were to be used, the idea being that when their upper surfaces became worn they could be turned and the other three faces used successively. The scheme was successfully opposed by the London & Birmingham and the Grand Trunk Railway Companies who insisted, not without reason, that the idea was unsound.

With the rapid spread of railways, interest in the fast road vehicle began to wane, and more than half a century was to pass by before the achievements of carriages such as Summers & Ogle's or Hill's were surpassed or even equalled. Unlike the railway companies, the road-vehicle builders were never powerful enough to overcome the opposition of the landowners whose interests lay in horses and the supply of fodder. The landowning interest controlled many of the Turnpike Trusts which raised the tolls on steam vehicles to a prohibitive level. Two pounds was levied on a steamer as against three shillings for a horse coach. By an Act of 1861 a uniform scale of tolls was imposed throughout the country and limitations on the size, weight and speed of steamers were laid down. Speed was to be restricted to 10 miles an hour in the country and 5 miles an hour through towns and villages, and at least two people must be in charge of each vehicle. This was followed by the famous, or infamous, Locomotive Act of 1865 which has passed into history under the popular title of the " Red Flag Act." This reduced the permissible speeds to 4 and 2 m.p.h. respectively. The clause in this Act which has immortalised it in popular memory read as follows :

" Firstly, at least three persons shall be employed to drive or conduct such locomotive, and if more than two waggons or carriages be attached thereto, an additional person shall be employed who shall take charge of such waggons or carriages.
" Secondly, one of such persons, while such Locomotive is in motion, shall precede such Locomotive on foot by not less than sixty yards and shall carry a red flag constantly displayed, and shall warn drivers of horses and riders of the approach of such Locomotive and shall signal the driver thereof when it is necessary to stop and shall assist horses, and carriages drawn by horses, passing the same."

It was to this clause that the enthusiastic autocarists of 1896 directed public attention in their campaign for legislative reform. Consequently it is widely and very naturally believed that until the Locomotives on Highways Act of 1896 secured reform it was still necessary for every mechanical road vehicle to be preceded by a man carrying a red flag. It is most curious to note, therefore, that in fact this Red Flag clause was amended by the Highways and Locomotives Act of 1878. The relevant passage in this Act reads as follows :

" Amendment of 28 and 29 Vict. c., sec. 3. The paragraph numbered ' Secondly ' of Section three of the Locomotives Act, 1865, is hereby repealed, so far as it relates to England, and in lieu thereof, the following paragraph is hereby substituted ; namely,

" Secondly, one of such persons, while the Locomotive is in motion, shall precede by at least twenty yards the Locomotive on foot, and shall in case of need assist horses, and carriages drawn by horses, passing the same."

From this it will be seen that although all vehicles must still be preceded by a man on foot, that man was no longer compelled to bear a red flag. Whether the campaigners of 1896 and the authorities whom they opposed were unaware of this amendment, or whether the former knew the true legal position but preferred to invoke the extinct red flag as a convenient and popular symbol for attack is a mystery which no one has ever explained. It is sufficient here to say that, red flag or no, until their repeal in 1896 these Acts most effectually crippled the development of the light, fast moving passenger vehicle on the English roads. Thomas Rickett of Castle Foundry, Buckingham was the last to build steam vehicles of this description on a commercial scale.

From *Steam on Common Roads* by A. Fletcher

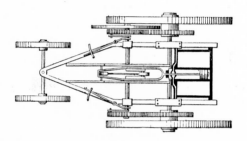

PLATE I

(*above*) *Trevithick's London Road Carriage, 1803 ; (below) Burstall and Hill's four-wheel drive carriage, 1825.*

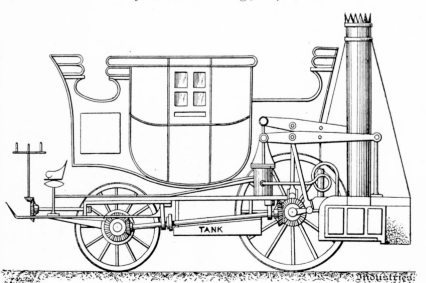

PLATE 2

(*above*) *Carrett's Steam Carriage "Fly-by-Night" 1861; (below) Mackenzie's Steam Brougham, 1874.*

For the next thirty-five years development was very largely restricted to the heavy, slow moving, road locomotive or traction engine designed mainly for agricultural use. This story need not concern us here except in one respect. This was the work of R. W. Thomson, a native of Stonehaven and at one time an employee of the Stephensons of railway fame.

On 10th December, 1845, Thomson took out a patent for a pneumatic tyre. This consisted of a hollow tube, or " elastic belt " as he called it, constructed of layers of canvas bonded with rubber solution. This tube was encased in an outer cover composed of a series of leather segments bolted to the wheel rim and riveted together over the tube. The tube was inflated with air by means of a small pipe which passed through the rim of the wheel and which could be sealed by an air-tight cap. In 1846 Thomson fitted his pneumatic tyres to a horse brougham and this vehicle is said to have covered over a thousand miles in the streets of London in six months on one set of tyres with complete success. It is indeed remarkable to reflect that over a century ago Thomson should have grasped the essential features of the invention which, probably more than any other, has made possible modern road transport. It is even more remarkable that in a comparatively few years this pioneer's work should have been so completely forgotten that in 1888 the pneumatic tyre was " re-invented " by John Boyd Dunlop.

Production difficulties and repressive legislation both contributed to the failure of Thomson's premature invention, and in 1867 we find him concentrating on the manufacture of steam road locomotives at Leith. Yet he still devoted much attention to the improvement of wheels and fitted many of his locomotives with solid indiarubber tyres.

These were not altogether successful. He never evolved a satisfactory method of attaching the tyres to the rims. Consequently the soft rubber, flattening under the weight of the heavy vehicle, became stretched and this in turn led to tyre creep, friction and overheating. The rubber was also badly cut by the rough road surfaces. Nevertheless, Thomson's solid tyres were a great advance on the cumbersome and elaborate " spring wheels " which represented the only other contemporary attempts to solve the same problem.

Of the few individual light steam-carriages which were constructed after 1860, those of Tangye, Carrett and Mackenzie deserve some description. In 1862, Messrs. Tangye of Birmingham constructed the steamer *Cornubia*. It was of simple and robust construction, was capable of over 20 m.p.h. and travelled many hundreds of miles. The firm intended to produce a number of similar vehicles, but as a result of the Acts of 1861 and 1865 they were forced to abandon the project.

In the same year that Tangye produced *Cornubia*, Mr. W. O. Carrett designed what was described as a " steam pleasure carriage " to the order of George Salt the celebrated mill-owner of Saltaire. This remarkable vehicle was built by the firm of Carrett, Marshall & Co., Sun Foundry, Leeds, and was exhibited at the Royal Show at Leeds in 1861 and at the London Exhibition in the following year. It had a locomotive type boiler, differential gear, and a clever arrangement of links which relieved the fork spindle of the single front wheel from the strain of road shocks. It is said to have performed very well and *Engineering* of June 1866 described it as " probably the most remarkable locomotive ever made." Apparently Mr. George Salt came to the conclusion that it would not be consonant with the dignity of his position to defy the law of 1861, for he gave his carriage away to a certain Mr. Frederick Hodges of Kent. This enterprising gentleman did not share Mr. Salt's scruples. He promptly christened the carriage *Fly-by-Night* and, in the words of *Engineering*, he " did fly, and no mistake, through the Kentish villages when most honest people were in their beds." Hodges' exploits were remembered in Kent for many years, and he achieved the feat of collecting six summonses in as many weeks, one of them for travelling at 30 m.p.h.

In 1874, H. A. O. Mackenzie of Scole made a steam brougham, the first steam passenger vehicle to be built in Norfolk. A Field type vertical boiler mounted at the rear supplied a two-cylinder engine which drove a countershaft through a two-speed gear. The gear on the countershaft embodied a differential, and the final drive to the wheels was by chain. The single front wheel was steered by tiller. It is said that the brougham ran quietly and smoothly at an average speed of 10–12 m.p.h., and that it covered many hundreds of miles, a circumstance which suggests that the local police force were amiably disposed towards Mr. Mackenzie. While this brougham did not demonstrate any considerable mechanical progress, its coachwork was markedly advanced. The driving compartment was totally enclosed, there being a glass windscreen forward and a side door with drop window. In summer, one feels that with the boiler simmering gently in the rear, the closed body may have become a little too cosy for comfort. Nevertheless, Mr. Mackenzie obviously took a more realistic view of the English climate than many vehicle builders who followed him and who did not hesitate to expose the unfortunate autocarist to the mercy of the elements from the knees upwards. Whereas it might be argued that some of the earlier steam carriages were the ancestors of the motor bus rather than the private car, Mackenzie's brougham, seating four persons, was unquestionably a private vehicle and it is a pity that its ultimate fate is not known.

The second steam car to be built in Norfolk is still preserved in private hands. Built by G. S. Soame, Perseverance Works, Marsham, it appeared on the road in 1902 and was registered AH 136 under the Road Traffic Act. Soame's car was virtually a mechanised wagonette with the addition of a lofty canopy. It was fitted with a two-speed gear of traction engine type which meant that the vehicle had to be stopped in order to change the ratios. Final drive from the countershaft to the wheels was by flat balata belting which was much given to slipping in wet weather. When we consider this vehicle it must be admitted that its design shows little advance upon, and in many respects compares unfavourably with that of steam carriages built sixty years before.

While France may justly name Joseph Cugnot as the pioneer of road locomotion, England soon surpassed the efforts of Continental engineers so that it is safe to claim that by 1860 the English road vehicle led the world. But by the last decades of the nineteenth century the initiative had once more passed to the Continent, to France and Germany, while in England many of the lessons learnt by practical experience in the bygone years of fruitful experiment had been forgotten and must needs be re-discovered. Such was the result of the Locomotive Acts ; and thus it came about that it was from over the Channel that the first commercially built, internal combustion engined cars came to challenge the supremacy of " unconquered steam " on the English highway.

CHAPTER TWO

THE COMING OF INTERNAL COMBUSTION

IT WAS IN 1860 that the Frenchman Lenoir patented the first gas engine, and two years later his countryman Beau de Rochas evolved the four-stroke cycle—explosion, exhaust, suction, compression—upon which principle the great majority of petrol engines operate. In 1876, Doctor N. A. Otto designed the famous " Otto Silent Gas Engine " which worked on the four-stroke cycle and which was built under licence by the Crossley Brothers in England.

Application of the new power to a road carriage was an obvious move, and the Austrian Siegfried Markus exhibited such a machine in Vienna as early as 1873. This vehicle has been preserved by the Austrian Automobile Club. On the question of whether Carl Benz or Gottlieb Daimler should take the credit for the first successful commercial application of the new power to a road vehicle historians disagree. Daimler, a technical director of the Otto works at Deutz, built a motor cycle in 1884, following this with a second motor cycle and a four-wheeled car in 1886. In the latter respect Daimler was narrowly beaten by his countryman Carl Benz who produced his first three-wheeled car in 1885. There is thus so little to choose between the inventive achievements of these distinguished Germans that they may reasonably be entitled to share the distinction of fathering the petrol driven car.

The first motor-car to be imported into England was a three-wheeled Benz built in 1888. These early German cars were very crude affairs. The single-cylinder horizontal engines were of open gas engine type mounted at the rear and driving a countershaft by two-speed flat belts. Final drive was by chain. France was responsible for the transformation of these first crude vehicles into a design which basically resembled the motor-car of today. Count De Dion and Monsieur Bouton superseded the slow speed horizontal engine with its exposed crankshaft by designing a compact vertical totally enclosed " high speed " engine which was the parent of the modern car engine.[1] Panhard & Levassor were the first to build a car in which the major components were arranged in a manner which was destined to become standard automobile practice. The twin-cylinder Daimler engine fitted to the first Panhards was mounted at the front of the chassis frame and drove through a clutch and exposed sliding change-speed gear to a differential. The differential, however, was arranged on a countershaft, final drive being by chain. The Renault Brothers, in 1894, were the first to incorporate the differential in the back axle, using a long propeller shaft and dispensing with chains.

In many respects these first petrol cars still compared unfavourably with the best steam carriages. They were neither so fast nor so reliable, and though much lighter their engines were of inadequate power and laboured along to the accompaniment of much noise and vibration. Two significant advances were made, however, almost at the outset. All but the earliest Benz cars were fitted with Ackermann steering in which the front wheels pivoted on

[1] It is only fair to add however, that Daimler also recognised the value of a higher engine speed, his 15-deg. V-twin engine running at 800-900 r.p.m., or more than twice the speed used by Benz.

short stub-axles attached to a fixed axle beam. This, even in its first crude form was a great improvement on the single front wheel or the swinging axle of the early steam carriages. The other great development was the successful application of the pneumatic rubber tyre. Thomson's invention had been re-discovered by John Boyd Dunlop in 1888, but although it was successfully applied to bicycles, it was not considered practicable for use on heavier vehicles. Consequently the earliest cars fitted wired-on tyres of solid rubber or " cushion " type. In 1895, however, the brothers Michelin confounded the sceptics by running a car fitted with " beaded edge " pneumatics in the Paris-Bordeaux race.

Nevertheless, despite this achievement some years were to elapse before the technique of tyre manufacture was developed to an extent that ensured reliability combined with reasonable tyre mileage. The first pneumatics caused the pioneer automobilist more trouble than any other component, trouble that was not made any lighter by the fact that, at the time of their introduction there were no such things as detachable wheels or even rims. A puncture consequently involved the removal of the tyre from the rim *in situ*. Of soft material, weak in the wall and of inadequate size in proportion to the weight of the car, the early tyres punctured readily on the rough road surfaces, frequently burst, particularly in hot weather, and were prone to stretch and fly off the rims. They were very costly and even at best they soon wore out. Charles Jarrott, in his classic book *Ten Years of Motors and Motor Racing*, has given us a graphic description of his first experience with pneumatic tyres. It was on a hot day and no sooner had he and S. F. Edge repaired one tyre than another burst. After this experience they were tempted to try a patent liquid preparation which, pumped into the tubes instead of air, claimed to eliminate trouble. At first all seemed to be well and Edge and Jarrott finished their day's run very elated. But when a start was made in the morning the curious motion of the car suggested that its wheels had become square. The horrid truth dawned upon them that the liquid in the tubes had solidified as it cooled overnight, leaving a considerable " flat " on that portion of the tyre which had taken the weight of the car. Yet despite all its early defects the pneumatic tyre came to stay. When they could be induced to hold air their advantage was so obviously overwhelming that Jarrott, Edge and their contemporaries preferred to wrestle with their diabolic behaviour rather than return to solids. Consequently in a very few years the pneumatic tyre became almost universal on all but the heaviest vehicles.

Although legislation made commercial production impossible, English inventors were not altogether idle in the period preceding the repeal of the Locomotive Acts. Several petrol engined vehicles were built privately in different parts of the country, their designers flouting the law in order to test their products. As early as 1887 F. H. Butler constructed a small tricycle with such advanced features as Ackermann steering, radiator cooling and electric ignition. Butler looked forward to a commercial future for his tricycles but by 1890 the authorities had successfully driven him off the road and compelled him to abandon his experiments.

In 1895 two cars appeared, one built by Messrs. Roots and Venables and the other by J. H. Knight the gas engine designer of Farnham. In October of that year Knight was fined in Farnham " for permitting a locomotive to be at work " without a licence, while in December another pioneer J. A. Koosen was fined one shilling and costs " for using a locomotive without causing a person on foot to precede it by at least twenty yards."

The publicity which both these cases received provided valuable material for the growing campaign for the repeal of the Locomotive Acts. By this time a number of influential people, notably the Honourable Evelyn Ellis, Mr. Hewetson and Sir David Salomons had imported Continental cars which they demonstrated on private roads and exhibited at Tunbridge Wells in October 1895. As a result of the interest thus stimulated the Self-Propelled Traffic Association was formed to press for repeal with Sir David Salomons as first President. At the same time and with the same purpose in view *The Autocar* magazine was launched by Mr. Henry Sturmy, inventor of the three-speed cycle gear. The campaign for repeal was soon successful for in November 1896 the Acts of 1865 and 1878 disappeared from the Statute Book. They were succeeded by the Locomotives on Highways Act which permitted cars to travel freely on the English roads provided their speed did not exceed 12 m.p.h.[1]

With this overdue reform a new era in the history of inland transportation dawned in England. Though the majority, if they had heard of the motor-car at all, regarded it as a rich man's impracticable toy, the members of the Self-Propelled Traffic Association were fully aware of the significance of the occasion. To celebrate " Emancipation Day ", as it was called, there was arranged that most historic of all English motoring events, the run from London to Brighton which took place on 14th November, 1896.

On the night of the 13th the competing cars assembled

---

[1] The Act originally permitted 14 m.p.h. but the Local Government Board were empowered to reduce this figure to 12 m.p.h.

at the Central Hall in readiness for the start from the Hotel Metropole on the morrow. They were a motley but distinguished collection of almost exclusively Continental or Transatlantic origin. The two Panhard et Levassor cars which had won the Paris–Bordeaux and the Paris–Marseilles races were there, H. J. Lawson, first President of the Motor Car Club having arranged to travel in one of them, while the Honourable Evelyn Ellis was driving a third Panhard. A towering German Daimler landaulette was present to conduct no less a personage than Herr Gottlieb Daimler himself. The great man certainly showed wisdom in providing himself with the only closed vehicle ; the rest offered their occupants no protection whatever from the raw rigours of an English November day. Most intrepid of all were those who purposed to travel as passengers on the curious but potent little Leon Bollee tricars ; for on these machines the passenger seat was placed between the front wheels and ahead of the driver, a position not merely exposed but highly vulnerable in the event of collision. Indeed, on the way to Brighton one Bollee did charge a hedge, catapulting its passenger neatly into the ditch.

America was represented by two Duryea cars and by that eccentric charlatan E. J. Pennington riding a tricycle of his own design which included such curious and suspect features as the " long, mingling spark " device which was causing much speculation in motoring circles at that time. There were also a number of electric vehicles, though precisely how they intended to reach Brighton was not clear. Vehicles of English manufacture with Continental engines were the Beeston Tricycle and the Arnold Motor Carriage. The latter is of particular interest in several respects. It claims to have been the first motor vehicle to run in Ireland ; it was fitted by its owner with an electric self-starter of dynamotor type, and it is the only 1896 entrant which has survived to appear regularly in the Commemoration Runs to Brighton organised by the R.A.C.

If from some corner of Paradise reserved for engineers Hill of Dartford looked down curiously on this concourse in the Central Hall a smile must surely be forgiven him. For with the exception of Leon and Amadée Bollee it is doubtful whether any of those present would have cared to challenge Hill's feat of travelling from London to Hastings and back in the day at twice the speed of a stage coach. Even to start the cars and bring them to the starting point was no mean feat, and in the early morning of the 14th the interior of the Central Hall must have resembled pandemonium. We may well imagine the confused clamour of excited French, German and English voices as the mechanicians furiously wound crank handles, pulled starting cords or rushed about in a gloom of exhaust smoke punctuated by the glare of petrol fires. For, owing to the absence of electrical ignition, ignition tubes must needs be pre-heated, while on a cold morning the fuel in the surface carburettors (the jet carburettor was still to come) was reluctant to vaporise. Consequently the process of starting from cold was usually spectacular. Charles Jarrott has described the method employed by his friend Frank Wellington for starting one of the Panhards : " He turned on the petrol tap, flooded the whole of the engine with petrol turned the tap off, lit a match, dropped it inside the bonnet of the motor and then ran away . . ." Jarrott was left to assure the terrified bystanders that the services of the fire-brigade were not required.

Before departing for Brighton the competitors breakfasted at the Hotel Metropole and in the course of this repast the Earl of Winchelsea tore up a red flag. In view of the legal position previously outlined, considerable mystery surrounds this piece of ritual but it was greeted with great acclamation by the company none the less. Breakfast over the competitors coaxed their cars into life once more and drove away through the misty London streets towards Brighton. Unfortunately there must have been a chronic lack of competent and disinterested observers along the route, for no one has ever given a clear account of what went on along the Brighton road on that memorable day. The two American Duryeas stoutly maintained their claim to be the first to arrive at Brighton whereas their fellow competitors alleged that, though they may indeed have arrived first, they never appeared at the start in London. It was suggested that they had been conveyed part of the way by train and had slipped surreptitiously into the procession *en route*. Certainly the official result did not uphold the Duryea claim. It read as follows :

		Time		
		h.	*m.*	*s.*
1.	Leon Bollee (Bollee)	3	44	35
2.	Amadée Bollee (Bollee)	4	0	20
3.	Panhard Wagonette No. 8.	5	1	10
4.	Lawson's Landau	6	7	30
5.	Panhard Dog-Cart No. 6.	6	8	15
6.	Sherrin's Electric Bath-chair	6	12	10
7.	Daimler Phaeton	6	12	25
8.	Pennington's Tricycle	6	17	0
9.	Bersey's Electric Landau	6	19	40
10.	Panhard	6	22	0

There seems little reason to doubt that the brothers Bollee were in fact the first to complete the course because their little tricars were undoubtedly the fastest petrol engined vehicles of the day. But the appearance of two electric vehicles among the first ten is a mystery which I have never seen explained. Did they change batteries *en route* or were they, like the Duryeas, conveyed by dishonest means ?

What was motoring really like in 1896 ? By far the best way of finding an answer to this question is to obtain a seat in one of the older veteran cars which, under the auspices of the R.A.C., annually make the pilgrimage from London to Brighton on the anniversary of the first historic event. Admittedly, roads and tyres are very different today, but this advantage is offset, despite their owners' careful pre-paration, by the advanced age of the cars. For several years running I drove to Brighton, not without vicissitudes, in a 1903 Humberette which I then owned, but this vehicle, though crude in many respects, was essentially a motor-car with its orthodox layout of clutch, gearbox, propeller shaft and live axle, and so belongs to a later chapter. I was anxious to make the journey in a real " horseless carriage," so that when, in 1938, a friend of mine acquired a vehicle of this description and asked me to accompany him to Brighton, I accepted with alacrity. The car was called, somewhat ominously, a Hurtu, but in actual fact it was a Benz built under licence in France and was thus a typical example of the earliest phase. In the hands of its previous owner it had been entered for the Brighton run on several occasions but had never finished the course. We were determined that on this occasion it should do so.

The car was mounted on spidery wheels with solid rubber tyres, the front wheels being much smaller than the back. At first glance there appeared to be a remarkable absence of essential machinery, but on lifting what seemed to be the lid of a boot at the back, the connecting rod and crankshaft of the single-cylinder horizontal engine were revealed, bristling with brass lubricators. The engine was mounted on the offside of the frame, and on the nearside the crank-shaft was extended to carry two floating pulleys of different sizes, each of which could be engaged by a sliding clutch between them which was moved by the gear lever. From these pulleys two flat belts took the drive forward to a countershaft which was connected to the rear axle by external sprockets and chains. There was a large water tank under the seat from which long pipes extended to the cylinder jacket and to a snake-like gilled radiator tube mounted low down between the front wheels. Engine speed was controlled by varying the exhaust valve lift while the inlet valve was automatic, which means to say that it was opened against a very light spring by the suction of the piston. Tube had been replaced by battery ignition, the only major departure from original practice. The end of the crankshaft extension protruded through the side of the body, and on it was mounted a small wooden pulley. Round this a cord could be wound for starting purposes on the same principle used today for marine outboard motors. With this arrangement, if the engine fired or failed to fire, all was well; but, as we soon discovered, in the by no means infrequent event of it back-firing, the unfortunate exponent was drawn forward by the rope to make forcible contact with the back of the vehicle.

We soon appreciated why the car had never reached Brighton, for although the engine started fairly readily and ran evenly, it produced no power at all. Only with difficulty could it be coaxed away from rest in low gear, while it would only pull top gear downhill or with the aid of a strong following wind. However, careful attention and adjustment had improved the performance considerably, before the time came to take the car on a trailer to the Cumberland Garage, Marble Arch, in readiness for the start in Hyde Park on the morrow.

Next morning the car behaved in the most exemplary fashion. Starting from rest, or changing from low to fast speed is always the tense moment in handling these early cars. It is impossible to synchronise engine speed control with the movement of gear or clutch, it is too insensitive, so the engine revs and the whole car trembles like a jelly. Then the gear is engaged, there is a forward jerk, the engine speed dies away and there is one loud TUFF from the exhaust ; will there be another, or is the engine going to stall ? If the engine does pick up the load, the expression of anxious concentration on the faces of the crew can be seen to change instantly to smiles of relief and self-congratulation. On the contrary, obvious indications that the engine is not equal to the burden suddenly thrust upon it are the signal for the passenger to dismount precipitately and push for all he is worth, leaping on again as best he may if his efforts show signs of being successful. On many cars with two speeds only, the gap between the two ratios is so great that a change to top can only be affected, without such assistance, on a dead level surface or with a following wind. Speed on low gear is so low, that in any other circumstances all forward momentum is lost by the time top is engaged. Often when driving my Humber I had ordered my passenger to give assistance when changing up, and now I was prepared to do the same. Much to my surprise, however, not once that morning did I leave my seat until we pulled in to the lunch-time stop at Crawley. The cars of later vintage which started after us flashed by one by one at what seemed to us a terrifying speed, but our old engine chugged along gallantly and never faltered. The weather was fine and dry so that the belts did not slip, and with the engine turning over slowly at 12 to 15 m.p.h. on top speed there was little vibration and travelling was extraordinarily pleasant. My driver's only moments of concern were occasioned by his efforts to keep our narrow wheels from engaging in the tram lines through Brixton whenever stationary vehicles forced him to swing across the tracks. By the time we reached Crawley we were feeling highly pleased with ourselves, but this was fated to be the pride which precedes a fall.

Drivers in the old Continental road races always believed that a long trouble-free run at the outset meant disaster later, and the longer their luck held the gloomier they became. This pessimistic belief was certainly justified in our case. In the first place, when our starting time came the engine refused to fire. Car after car chugged merrily off on its way to Brighton while we tugged fruitlessly at the starting cord. Then we pushed the car up and down the main street of the town. Watched by a curious ring of small boys, we lit a succession of bonfires on the pavement, in which we repeatedly pre-heated the sparking plug. The last car had long ago departed when at last, suddenly and quite unaccountably, the engine started. But when we set off up the long slope in the direction of Brighton it at once became apparent that the engine had lost all the extra power we had infused into it and had reverted to its original weak state. Nothing was obviously wrong so we decided that it was best to push on as best we might rather than lose more time in tinkering with it. Slowly and laboriously the car struggled up the long hill and had just reached the summit when there was a sudden sound of rushing water and the entire contents of the large water tank under our seat gushed out into the road. Vibration had split the

PLATE 3

(*above*) *Mr. Knight's Petroleum Tricycle*, 1895 ; (*below*) *The first Benz imported into England*, 1893.

PLATE 4

(above) At the first Motor Exhibition ever held in England, Tunbridge Wells, 15th October, 1895 ; the Hon. Evelyn Ellis in his Panhard et Levassor; (below) The "Emancipation Day" run to Brighton, November, 1896. H. J. Lawson and his Secretary Charles Turrell are seated at the tillers of the two Panhards.

flexible connection of one of the long water pipes. This was quickly replaced and the tank refilled from a neighbouring public house. The engine re-started at once this time, and we were off again. On every down gradient we made all the speed we could, swaying along in the most reckless fashion at 25 m.p.h. and hoping that nothing lurked round the corners which would necessitate an emergency stop. But as soon as we reached the level the engine died away, while the slightest adverse gradient brought us down to low gear assisted, more often than not, by my efforts in the rear. On one of our rapid descents a sudden shriek announced that one of the countershaft bearings was seizing, and at intervals for the rest of our journey I would hang over the side with a can feeding it with oil. More alarming still, the shaft had developed so much end-play that the driving sprocket occasionally floated out and hit the rim of the rear wheel with a horrid sound. To add to our troubles it now began to rain heavily and continuously from a leaden sky so that, having no hood or screen to protect us, we were soon soaked to the skin, for no mackintosh seems capable of protecting the crew of a horseless carriage under such conditions. We feared that the wet might affect our ignition system, but in one respect it did us a service for it caused the driving belts to slip, not too much but just enough to lower our gear ratios a little which was all to the good.

As we rattled down the hill towards Bolney cross-roads I could see ahead, indistinct in the failing light and driving rain, the long skyline of the South Downs. I knew then that if only we could reach the summit of that last stiff climb at Pyecombe we stood a good chance of finishing, for from that point onwards it was easy going, being nearly all down hill. But our engine's powers seemed to be failing rapidly, and its exhaust note, an energetic tuff-tuff-tuff when we had started so bravely that morning (so long ago it seemed) was now no more than a tired sigh. At last we reached the foot of the hill and I at once jumped down and began to push. I pushed desperately for I felt that if once the engine stalled it would never start again. I was almost exhausted and the engine was still slowing when several pairs of willing hands appeared beside mine, and our united efforts took the car over the top. The engine then began to pick up, I jumped aboard, in went top speed and we were away. We passed between the stone pillars which mark the Brighton boundary ; we traversed the suburbs ; we sighted the fantastic domes and minarets of the Prince Regent's Pavilion, and then we heard the sound of the sea and knew that we had finished. It was still teeming with rain ; it was almost dark and we carried no lights ; our fellow competitors were already being entertained to tea by the Lord Mayor in the Pavilion. Yet none of these things seemed to matter in the least for we had reached Brighton.

This was motoring as it was in the days when Queen Victoria still sat upon the throne of England, and I feel sure that those who took part in that first historic drive down the Brighton road in 1896 experienced misfortunes very similar to ours, and knew the same alternating feelings of hope and despair culminating, if fortune favoured them, in the exhilaration of achievement won against odds. Yet already, in 1896, the days when a journey from London to Brighton was a daring adventure were numbered, so rapid was the acceleration of technical development. Five years later the death of the old Queen closed a chapter in English history as great as it was long. In the brief Edwardian heyday which followed, the motor car ceased once and for all to be a horseless carriage and assumed its own distinctive and definitive form. Freaks and mechanical vagaries there still might be, but the Edwardian car at its best was as reliable as its ancestors were temperamental. Yet I sometimes wonder if the nineteenth century driver of the horseless carriage, whether he lived at the beginning of the century in the age of steam, or at the end of it when the age of internal combustion had dawned, should not be envied above all subsequent users of the road. Human nature is such that man can only find true satisfaction in achievement that is dearly bought by risk, disappointment and high endeavour. The modern motorist buzzing down to Brighton in his little mass-produced saloon can never share the feelings of those who went before him. Bored, he fumbles for the switch of his car radio set.

CHAPTER THREE

LOST CAUSES

BEFORE PASSING ON to a consideration of the evolution of the orthodox motor-car in Edwardian England, those other sources of motive power, electricity and steam, which were overwhelmed in the triumphant progress of the internal combustion engine, deserve some notice. At the same time various other minor departures from the orthodox may also be briefly mentioned.

The first electric vehicle to be produced in England was designed by J. K. Starley who was responsible for the introduction of the safety bicycle and who was later to be associated with the Rover Company. This little car was built at the Meteor Works, West Orchard, Coventry, in 1888. It resembled a Bath chair and ran at 8 m.p.h.

The first successful commercial maker of electric vehicles was W. H. Bersey, and a number of omnibuses, cabs, vans, broughams and phaetons were produced to his designs during the '90s. The motors and accumulators used in these early vehicles were built by the pioneer electrical firm of Elwell-Parker at Wolverhampton.

Despite its limited range and the great weight of its batteries the electric vehicle enjoyed a considerable vogue as a town carriage, particularly in London where charging facilities were more readily available. The new motor-cars might appeal to young gentlemen of the '90s, anxious to cut a dash, and even to a few venturesome and heavily veiled members of the fair sex. But a vehicle which was smelly, noisy and unreliable and which spent its working life in a state of quivering animation was hardly a suitable mode of conveyance for the polite calls of a Dowager Duchess or for the rounds of a discreet and expensive Harley Street physician. The smoothness and silence of the electric vehicle, on the other hand, could scarcely offend the susceptibilities of the most dignified and conservative Victorian. Thus it came about that the elegant electric brougham, with a crest on the door panels and accompanied by a smart but staid driver who remained more of a coachman than a chauffeur, assumed a place in fashionable society from which it was not banished until Sir Henry Royce taught the motor-car good manners.

When, in 1947, I was being shown round the outbuildings of a large mansion in the north of England I was surprised and delighted to find, standing in the coach house, an electric brougham in perfect running order. Age had crazed the once mirror-smooth varnish of the body panels, but years of polishing had given them a lovely surface, dull yet lustrous, which exactly matched the bloom of the original black leather mudguards. The interior, beautifully upholstered in Bedford cord, had that subtle, slightly musty smell which always seems to characterise the work of the craftsman coachbuilder. The stronger odours of internal combustion banished it from all but a very few luxury limousines where it lingered in a rear compartment insulated by a division. Of all our five senses the sense of smell is, I think, the most evocative. At once it will conjure up nostalgic memories or rouse our imagination. Thus when I looked into the interior of this brougham I instantly recalled long-forgotten journeys in horse cabs, usually the exciting prelude to a seaside holiday. It evoked, too, in imagination, the days when the brougham was new but

when I was unborn. The '90s ; gaslight and the jingle of
hansoms ; Daly's ; the swing of full skirts to the waltz ;
Oscar Wilde scintillating at the dinner table and a fictional
Sherlock Holmes snugly ensconced in Baker Street. It all
seemed to linger there in that musty, dim little interior.
" Do you ever use it ? " I asked. The old nobleman shook
his head sadly. Like his elegant brougham, he belonged to
a different age. " I seldom drive it outside the grounds," he
said, and then, with pathetic dignity, he added, " Today I
am a hawk pursued by sparrows." He shut the doors of the
coach house and we walked in silence across the courtyard.
The great house did not watch us for shutters had closed its
eyes against the new world ; it held the memorials of the
past within it jealously like the memories of a dream that
sight would soon dispel.

It is hard to believe that the sedate electric brougham
could ever be transformed into a racing vehicle, yet such was
the case. The young " blood " of the '90s might consider
his petrol car *the* sporting vehicle, but on the roads of
France it was the electric car in the hands of Camille
Jenatzy and the Comte de Chasseloup-Laubat which captured the first officially recognised flying kilometre records
in 1898 and 1899. Chasseloup-Laubat set up the first record
in December '98, at 39.24 m.p.h. but by April of the following year Jenatzy had raised it to 65.79 m.p.h. and had thus
achieved the distinction of being the first man to travel on
the common road at a speed of over a mile a minute.

Perhaps it is unfair to describe the electric car as a " lost
cause " because it has enjoyed an uninterrupted career as a
light commercial vehicle for short distance deliveries which
involve very frequent stopping and starting. In this sphere
its employment has increased in recent years thanks to
improved batteries and better and more widespread facilities

for re-charging. The modern petrol shortage has even led to the introduction of an electric estate or " utility " car. But limited range, the weight of the batteries and the amount of space they occupy still disqualify the electric car as a long distance vehicle. Unless we evolve a revolutionary method of storing electricity or of " broadcasting " it through the ether from power station to motor, the electric car is unlikely ever again to challenge the orthodox motor car.

" Unconquered steam " did not submit without a struggle to the new force of internal combustion. In 1894 a De Dion Bouton steam car was the first to finish in the Paris–Rouen race although it was only awarded second place, a Serpollet steamer being third. Three years later the Comte de Chasseloup-Laubat won the Marseilles–Nice race with a De Dion steamer at an average of 18.8 m.p.h. for the 146 miles. In April, 1902, at Nice, Monsieur Serpollet, driving a steam car of his own make, broke Jenatzy's mile-a-minute record with a speed of 75.06 m.p.h. Shortly afterwards the Serpollet was one of only three cars to finish in the heavy class in the Circuit du Nord over a course of 540 miles.

The earliest steam cars to be imported to England from the Continent and America were, like their electric and petrol-engined counterparts, true horseless carriages in appearance, the Locomobile of the '90s, for example, being similar in general outline to the Benz. But when the petrol car assumed a conventional shape of its own, the steam car followed suit with the result that the two types remained superficially indistinguishable. In the case of the steamer, the forward mounted radiator became the condenser while, except on the White and the Serpollet, the bonnet housed the boiler, the engine being mounted horizontally in the rear of the chassis, usually in unit with the

back axle. There being no need for a clutch or for reverse
and variable speed gears, the drive to the wheels was either
direct or through a fixed reduction gear. The engine of the
White steamer was vertical and mounted under the bonnet,
driving through a conventional propeller shaft, while the
flash boiler was mounted under the driving seat. The
Serpollet had a four-cylinder horizontally opposed poppet-
valve engine in front and a flash boiler in the boot at the
rear.

Many of the earlier steam cars exhausted to atmosphere,
but later, to ensure silent running and to conserve water,
an exhaust steam condenser was fitted which resembled
the radiator of the petrol car. It was not practicable, however, to make this " radiator " large enough to act as a true
condenser, that is to say to create a vacuum and so increase
the efficiency of the engine. On the contrary it was merely a
water economiser which was apt to reduce power by creat-
ing back pressure when the engine was working hard. For
this reason the White was fitted with a by-pass valve which
enabled the driver to divert the exhaust steam to atmosphere
when road conditions called for the maximum power.
Boilers were either of vertical multitubular or flash type.
Reduced to the simplest terms, the flash boiler consists of a
coil of pipe enclosed in a combustion chamber. Water is
pumped in at one end and emerges at the other in the form
of high-pressure steam. This flash coil, as it is usually called,
is thus at once feed-water heater, boiler and superheater.
For use in a car its great advantages are its small size and
weight and its ability to generate steam almost instan-
taneously. But it has one great disadvantage. Having no
steam storage space, the quantity of steam it can supply is
wholly dependent on the quantity of water pumped into
the coil combined with the intensity of heat in the combus-

tion chamber. Under the conditions of road travel where demands for steam are constantly varying and may call for a closed throttle one second and full throttle the next, even the least technically minded will appreciate that the co-ordinated control of the feed pump and burners must be extremely delicate and responsive ; otherwise there will be a most unfortunate delayed action effect. Similarly, if pump and burners do not act in concert the flash coil may be either flooded or overheated. No doubt the pioneers Burstall and Hill experienced this difficulty with their " heat generator " of 1824, and it is one which can scarcely be said ever to have been entirely overcome. [1] It is significant that the Stanley brothers, who continued to build steam cars in America long after production had ceased in Europe, never used the flash system.

Undoubtedly the most successful Edwardian flash steam cars were the Serpollet and the American White. The latest White cars were most imposing and luxurious vehicles with a fine performance. One of these cars and a " Silver Ghost " Rolls Royce took part in a trial over a 1,000-mile course, mostly in Scotland. That there was little to choose between the performance of the two cars in this event is an eloquent tribute to the White. The steamer only suffered one involuntary stoppage, and the explanation of this has a nice contemporary ring about it. A small tap was damaged by a passenger's foot " when struggling to erect the cape-cart hood in a gale of wind."

British engineers were the discoverers of steam power and have always claimed, with some justification, to be the master makers of steam plant. It is therefore chastening to reflect that of the many steam cars to be seen on the roads

---

[1] The Serpollet automatic donkey pump metering both water and fuel was probably the most successful effort.

of England in the period preceding the first world war, almost all were either of American or Continental manufacture. There was, it is true, the Turner-Meisse flash steamer. But although this car was built in Wolverhampton by the predecessors of the present Turner Manufacturing Company, it was of Belgian design. The only light passenger steam car wholly designed and built in England was the Lifu of which a limited number were built in 1901. The manufacturers were the Liquid Fuel Company of the Isle of Wight, makers of heavy steam vehicles and steam launches. The specification of the Lifu resembled that of the American Stanley in that a firetube boiler fired by a paraffin burner was located under the bonnet while the two-cylinder engine with Stephenson's Link motion was mounted horizontally, driving the rear wheels through a fixed reduction ratio. The Lifu engine, however, was a compound and the working pressure was 250 lb. per sq. in.

As few people in England today have ever seen, much less travelled in, a steam car, some description of a 1921 Stanley which a friend of mine once owned may be of some interest. The car was an open four-seater, and resembled the typical American " roadster " of the period. So close was this resemblance, in fact, that it had embarassing consequences. Leaving the car in a Birmingham street one day, the owner luckily returned in the nick of time to find a crowd assembled (all standing at a safe distance) while police and firemen were approaching the car warily but purposefully. A wisp of steam drifting through the bonnet louvres and a flicker of light from the pilot burner had convinced them that a spectacular conflagration was imminent.

The vertical boiler under the bonnet was fired by a vaporising burner (i.e., on the primus principle) which resembled an enlarged gas-ring. Like a Primus, paraffin was the fuel, but the pilot burner which heated the vaporising tube and was used to maintain pressure when the car was at rest, burnt petrol. Both fuels were supplied from pressure tanks under the driving seat. The two-cylinder simple engine with Stephenson's Link motion was mounted horizontally in the rear of the chassis and drove the rear wheels through a reduction gear. [1] A lever controlling the link motion had three positions : full gear for starting or for climbing exceptional gradients, a fixed cut-off position for normal running, and reverse.

Starting the car from cold was a slow and rather tedious process. Pressure was pumped into the petrol tank and a match applied to the pilot burner through a " peep-hole " in the burner casing. Then the driver sat in the driving seat solemnly pumping pressure into the paraffin tank by means of a pump lever in the cockpit which resembled a handbrake lever, the while he gazed hopefully at the fuel and steam pressure gauges on the dashboard. So soon as the vaporiser tube was hot enough the main burner ignited, and in approximately fifteen minutes the maximum working pressure of 600 lb. per sq. in. was reached. At this point, if there was no demand for steam, the main burner was extinguished automatically, re-igniting so soon as pressure fell. Once under way, too, a mechanical pump supplied pressure to the fuel tanks.

This protracted starting process would not be popular in our age of hurry when the average motorist is apt to lose patience if his engine does not respond to the first touch on the starter button, but once steam was up the steamer driver reaped an ample reward for his efforts. Despite all the skill and ingenuity which the motor industry

[1]The Stanley reduction ratio varied on different models from as low as 30:56 to as high as 51:57.

has expended on the internal combustion engine and on improved forms of transmission I can testify that a car which can rival that old Stanley of 1921 for silence and smoothness of operation has yet to be built. In manœuvring the steamer was almost uncanny, gliding out of the garage either forwards or backwards as the case might be without the slightest jerk or effort and to the accompaniment of a just audible sound which can best be likened to that produced by jerking forward the striking face of a matchbox over a smooth surface. Even this small sigh of steam exhausting into the condenser was only apparent at the slowest speeds ; running normally on the road all evidence of mechanical motion vanished. Petrol-engined cars have been christened " Ghost," " Phantom," " Wraith " or " Magic Carpet " to emphasise the quality of their performance, but I am bound to say that, fine though that performance undoubtedly is, it does not compare with the magic of steam. Although it is so long ago, I have never forgotten how we sailed along the Worcestershire roads with only the rush of the wind and the singing of the tyres in our ears. Hill-climbing was the most exhilarating and uncanny experience of all as the throttle pedal went down and without any apparent effort the Stanley seemed to be lifted over the gradient as though she had suddenly been given a tremendous push by ghostly hands. On one hill, I remember, we overhauled a small car buzzing fretfully along in third gear like an angry wasp. I can still see the look of almost fearful astonishment on the driver's face as an unpretentious American touring car swept past as though drawn up on an invisible wire.

This particular Stanley was known as the 10 h.p. model, and it was not a fast car : 40–45 m.p.h. was its maximum cruising speed, for although an ample reserve of power was available for hills or for short bursts, its use could not be sustained without exceeding the steaming capacity of the boiler. Two models of Stanley were manufactured, and I believe that the practice of steam enthusiasts in the States was to fit the boiler out of the larger 20 h.p. model into the smaller chassis. This was done by the Stanley brothers themselves in 1906 when steam flung down its last great challenge to the internal combustion engine.

It was a case of David and Goliath for the world's speed record holder at that time was Hemery who, in the previous December had thundered down a road at Arles in a Darracq of 200 h.p. at 109.65 m.p.h. In striking contrast to this intractable and terrifying monster, the steam challenger was virtually a standard car. It weighed 1,600 lb. and, apart from the larger boiler pressed to 1,000 lb. steam pressure, the only substantial alteration was in the transmission which had been changed from a reduction to a " step-up " of 1 : 2. The result was still docile and tractable, and Marriott drove the car from the Stanley works to Ormonde beach where he put up the astonishing speed of 121.52 m.p.h. this being the average for the flying kilometre in both directions.

Encouraged by this success, the Stanleys resolved to aim still higher. Various modifications were made, the car was lightened and the steam pressure raised to 1,300 lb. Then Marriott drove again on Ormonde beach. On his first run he is reputed to have reached a speed of 180 m.p.h. but on the return run, when travelling at an estimated speed of 190 m.p.h. the car suddenly became uncontrollable, dashed into the sea and overturned, decanting as it did so both the unfortunate driver and the boiler. Marriott had a miraculous escape except for the fact that one of his eyes had left its socket. This was replaced by a doctor on the spot and he regained perfect sight. The disaster is understandable, for the chassis design, suspension and brakes of 1906 cannot have been equal to such a terrific performance. After this experience the Stanley brothers decided that the risks involved were too great to warrant further attempts and so the power of steam has never again challenged internal combustion.

The last steam car which I saw on English roads was an American Doble in 1934. It was a large and impressive two-seater coupé which resembled a Continental rather than an American car. It belonged to Mr. Doble himself who was at that time in this country in connection with a project to build commercial vehicles and rail cars on the Doble system. This proved a failure although a Doble lorry was built which followed the example of the legendary *Fly-by-Night* by securing numerous summonses for speeding, while a rail car worked for a time on the Devil's Dyke branch of the Southern Railway. Though I never enjoyed the privilege of travelling in the Doble car, I saw it in action on several occasions, travelling with the same effortless smoothness and silence as the Stanley. Starting the Doble from cold, however, merely occupied seconds where the Stanley took minutes, for the former used a flash steam generator. The flash coil enclosed a combustion chamber which was supplied with a mixture of atomised diesel oil and air on a principle not dissimilar from that of the Mercedes system of supercharging which will be mentioned in a subsequent chapter. In this case a Sirocco fan blew air through the venturi of a " carburettor." Ignition of the mixture in the combustion chamber was produced initially by a normal sparking plug and high-tension coil. Dashboard switches brought electric pumps and ignition into action, and in less than a minute a tell-tale light signified that the car was ready to move off. The engine was a four-cylinder compound mounted in the same manner as that of the Stanley.

The Doble, despite its size, is said to have had a remarkable performance, accelerating with great rapidity from a standstill to a maximum of 90 m.p.h. Nevertheless, it would seem that those difficulties inherent in the use of the flash steam generator were not solved with complete success, while the atomising burner gave trouble, working better on paraffin than on diesel oil.

Advocates of the internal combustion engine argue that the energy latent in the fuel should be released where its power is required—in the cylinder—and that to translate that energy into steam and then introduce the steam to the cylinder is a needlessly cumbersome process. The steam engineer, however, replies that to create a violent explosion in a cylinder is a barbarous principle and a disgrace to the traditions of mechanical engineering. He regards the orthodox poppet valve gear of the petrol engine as equally crude in principle (which it is), while the near red-hot exhaust pipe offends a mind schooled to utilise all waste heat. When he goes on to dilate upon the efficiency of the modern steam unit, its smoothness, silence and flexibility, its great starting torque which eliminates any need for complicated transmission systems, and the consequent simplicity of control, we are left wondering why road transport should ever have been monopolised by so crude a type of prime mover. Why, we ask, has the steam car become a lost cause? There are still engineers who would reply that it is not a lost cause, and that the steam car may one day return.

There can be little doubt that the practical engineering problem of constructing a steam car which would compare favourably with the present-day motor-car could be solved without undue difficulty. Metallurgical developments, improved electrical auxiliaries and lubricating oils capable of withstanding a very high degree of superheating would all contribute to that solution. But commercially the possibility is remote. Not only would the new car confront an enormous vested interest and a public educated to accept the internal combustion engine, but the servicing problem would be immense. Reduced to its bare essentials the principle of the steam car is simple enough, but before it is capable of competing with the petrol engine for ease and rapidity in starting from cold and simplicity of operation, complex automatic auxiliaries such as water and fuel pumps, thermostatically and pressure controlled switches have to be introduced. It was in the matter of these auxiliary controls that the steam car builders of the past failed, for their ingenious efforts never matched the simplicity and reliability achieved, albeit crudely, by the petrol engine builders. Even if it is agreed that these problems could be successfully solved today, the result would still be a piece of mechanism at least as complicated as the petrol engine and totally different. Consequently no garage, accustomed to motor-cars which become more uniform in design every year, would be capable of servicing the steam car. On the other hand, no firm launching what would almost certainly be a car produced in limited numbers in the medium or high-priced class could possibly afford to establish beforehand its own nation-wide service organisation.

Another obstacle which the steam car builders failed to overcome, and which might prove just as formidable today, was the popular prejudice against high pressure steam. The uninitiated passenger would eye the steam pressure gauge on the dashboard askance (especially, in the case of the White, if they realised that they were sitting on top of the

PLATE 5
" The Elegant Electric Brougham."

PLATE 6

PROGRESS OF STEAM

(*above*) *The Lifu steam car of* 1901; (*below*) *The Doble steam car.*

PLATE 7

CURIOSITIES

(above) The Sunbeam Mabley ; (below) The Wolseley Gyro-car.

PLATE 8

(*above*) *The Lanchester Phaeton of* 1896. *The first four-wheeled petrol car ever built in England*; (*below*) *The First Wolseley car* 1895–6, *designed by Herbert Austin.*

boiler) and ask the inevitable question : " Suppose the boiler burst ? " In vain did the engineers point out that this event was highly improbable and that even if it did occur the result would not be catastrophic because the magnitude of a boiler explosion depends on volume and not pressure. Thus the explosion of a large Lancashire boiler at a pressure of 25 lb. per sq. in. is a major disaster whereas the fracture of a flash steam coil at a pressure of 1,500 lb. produces no lethal result. In their endeavour to overcome this unreasoning prejudice, the Stanley brothers once tested one of their vertical multitubular boilers to destruction. With the burner working and every outlet closed, the boiler was lowered down a dry well, a long pipe being attached to a pressure gauge on the surface. The pressure had risen to over 2,000 lb. per sq. in. before the sound of escaping steam was heard and pressure remained constant until the burners were cut off. The boiler was then hauled up when it was found that the top tube plate had lifted clear of the tubes and had thus acted as a safety valve. But, alas, these efforts to educate the general public were of little avail. The majority continued to regard the steam-car boiler or the flash steam generator as a bomb which might blow them into the next world at any moment.

Thus it has come about that the steam car is today a lost cause. A handful of enthusiasts continues to maintain old steam cars or to build experimental cars, but commercially the vehicle whose lineage extends back to the days of Richard Trevithick is dead and unlikely ever again to be reborn.

The 1930s witnessed the rapid development of the high-speed compression ignition, or " diesel " engine as it is popularly called, and its successful application to commercial vehicles. The modern high-speed diesel engine combines a good low-speed torque with remarkable fuel economy and great reliability. But, compared with a petrol engine of equivalent power, its first cost is greater, while it is heavier, rougher and less flexible. When fuel oil was untaxed and could be obtained for as little as 4d. per gallon motorists were prepared to tolerate the vibration and the somewhat ponderous performance of the diesel in return for the immense saving in running costs which it offered. Many will recall the Bentley fitted with a Gardner diesel engine which appeared at Shelsley Walsh and other motoring events, or the smaller Perkins engine which was then offered to private motorists as a replacement unit. When taxation increased the cost of fuel oil the economy of the diesel engine was no longer sufficient to outweigh its disadvantages for private car use. Unless economic circumstances change we are unlikely to see any serious invasion of the private car market by the compression ignition engine. Even if the use of fuel oil instead of petrol in cars were to be encouraged, the introduction of a low compression solid injection engine with electrical ignition, as developed in America, seems the more likely answer.

Other departures from the orthodox have been the cars fitted with engines operating on the two-stroke cycle which have appeared from time to time. The Fiat concern in Italy and Murray Jamieson in England developed two-stroke engined racing cars but, although remarkable power output was obtained, cooling and other technical difficulties prevented them from achieving any success in long-distance racing. The only commercially successful two-stroke English car was the Trojan. This ingenious design, developed by a subsidiary of Leyland Motors, employed a horizontal two-cylinder engine, a two-speed epicyclic gear and final drive by chain. The early models were unique in possessing solid rubber tyres, and the engine was started by means of a hand lever in the cockpit. The aim of the design was to produce a cheap and reliable utility car with low running and upkeep costs, and this the Trojan certainly fulfilled with remarkable success. But its performance was too mediocre and its behaviour too crude to please the majority of private motorists and it was in the form of a light delivery van that the chassis proved most popular. The fact that a few of these vans can still be seen on the road is a tribute to the soundness of the Trojan design. The only modern representatives of the two-stroke principle to be seen in England are the German D.K.W., the Lloyd and the miniature Bond.

In both world wars the resulting petrol shortage focused attention on the possibility of running cars on gas. One of my earliest recollections is of seeing, during the 1914–18 war, a closed car with a bellying gas envelope on its roof which could be replenished from the town gas supply. In the more recent war attention turned to producer-gas units and a number of cars were to be seen with gas generators either installed on the back of the chassis or mounted on a light two-wheeled trailer. Gas, whether it is derived from town supply or from a producer has a much lower thermal efficiency than petrol which means that power is much reduced. Moreover despite the use of " scrubbers," as they are called, in producer plants to purify the gas given off, it remains strongly acidic with the result that the rate of cylinder wear is practically doubled in the average engine. Unless methods of producing and cleaning gas can be considerably simplified and improved it is doubtful whether the principle will ever be widely applied either for private or commercial road transport except in emergency.

So much for the noteworthy departures from the orthodox. There has been no lack of still-born freak designs for which revolutionary claims were made by their sponsors but which need not detain us here. In concluding this chapter, however, two cars deserve a brief mention on account of their extreme oddity.

The Sunbeam Mabley which appeared in 1903 achieved a unique one-two-one wheel arrangement. It was a two-seater in which both driver and passenger sat sideways, one behind the other, one facing the near and the other the offside. The body, in fact, precisely resembled that peculiar type of Victorian sofa which was known as a " Sociable " though why it was so called is inexplicable since a more unsociable piece of furniture would be hard to conceive. The driver steered this odd vehicle by means of a tiller and must have developed a permanent crick in the neck in his efforts to face the line of travel. I have never heard any satisfactory explanation of the design of the Sunbeam Mabley. Was originality at any price the aim, or was it simply the result of a designer's brainstorm ?

Perhaps the most remarkable car ever made in this country was the two-wheeled Wolseley. When I was a schoolboy I possessed a stirring story of adventure entitled *The Cruise of the Gyro Car*, but it never occurred even to my optimistic mechanical mind that such a fabulous vehicle actually existed ; nor did such a possibility, I am sure, occur to the author. The gyro car belonged to the same category as the Space Ships, Moon Rockets, Death Rays and Flying Submarines beloved of the boys' magazine serials—or so I thought until I saw the two-wheeled Wolseley.

Just before the 1914 war a wealthy, and possibly eccentric, Russian Count approached the Wolseley Company stating that he required a motor car capable of travelling over the narrow paths on his large estate. Since money appeared to to be no object, the Company courageously set to work to meet their customer's requirements. The result of their efforts was a four-seater car powered by a four-cylinder side-valve engine and running upon two wheels placed in line ahead. Equilibrium was maintained by a large gyro fly-wheel revolving under the front seats. Two small wheels resembling enlarged chair castors were mounted amidships and upon either side of the car and could be lowered to support it when at rest with the gyro stopped. When completed, the car passed through its running tests with complete success and caused no small sensation. As might be imagined, the car displayed some curious characteristics. One which never failed to bewilder passengers was that when they stepped on the running board, instead of giving under their weight, the car lifted slightly owing to the reaction of the gyroscope.

From the financial point of view this unique enterprise had a sad ending. When war broke out the Count disappeared and nothing more has been heard of him from that day to this. Whether he thought twice about his order or became a victim of the Russian revolution will never be known. The gyro car never left the Wolseley works. In fact it was buried until 1936 when it was disinterred and restored to a place of honour. I hope it will continue to be suitably preserved and that one day, perhaps, some intrepid enthusiast may be permitted to set it in motion once again. It would certainly be a notable addition to the ranks of the " Edwardian " cars which have become such a feature of current motoring events.

CHAPTER FOUR

EDWARDIAN BAROQUE

THE BIRTH OF the British Motor Industry which followed the Emancipation Day run to Brighton was not auspicious. Among the pioneers attendant upon that birth the remarkable figure of Harry J. Lawson stands first. Of Lawson's enthusiasm for the new form of transport and his energy in popularising it in England there can be no question. He had played a leading part in the campaign for the repeal of the " Red Flag " Act; he was responsible for the importation of a number of Continental cars; he founded the first car club which was known as " A Society for the Protection, Encouragement and Development of the British Motor Industry "; he was the Chairman of this body and even designed for its members an ornate uniform which a contemporary described as being not unlike that of an Admiral of the Fleet. Through this Society, Lawson was responsible for the first motor exhibition at the Imperial Institute and for organising the Emancipation Day run to Brighton. Yet these multifarious activities were by no means disinterested but were all calculated primarily to advance Lawson's financial schemes. An indefatigable promoter of companies, Lawson had already exploited the boom which followed the invention of the safety bicycle, and in the manufacture of the new horseless carriages he saw a much wider and more fruitful field for his activities. Nothing if not ambitious, he planned to secure a complete monopoly of the motor industry in

England by forming a Company for the purpose of buying up all the relevant master patents. To this end the British Motor Syndicate was formed in 1895 and acquired patent rights from Daimler, Panhard Levassor, De Dion et Bouton, Leon Bollee and others. The next step was the flotation of subsidiary companies to manufacture cars under licence from the Syndicate and for this purpose the Daimler Company and the Great Horseless Carriage Company (later called the Motor Manufacturing Company) were formed and installed in the old Coventry Cotton Mills which Lawson bought and renamed the Motor Mills. Elsewhere in Coventry one of Lawson's earlier flotations, the Humber Cycle Company, now turned their attention to motor cycles and cars.

To follow in detail the vicissitudes and intricacies of Lawson's schemes would be wearisome. Suffice it to say that they failed, although the names of Daimler and Humber survived and ultimately flourished. The reason for that failure was that Lawson, no technician himself, was unfortunate in his choice of co-directors and engineers. For fabulous sums Lawson acquired some of the best vehicles the continent could produce, many of them road race winners, to serve as prototypes for his manufacturing companies. Already these cars embodied the fruits of several years practical experience on the road, but the English engineers would not concede technical superiority to any other nation and failed to take advantage of this experience. Too proud to copy, they must needs improve and experiment according to their own preconceived ideas. As a result thousands of pounds were squandered on the production of vehicles which proved markedly inferior in performance and reliability to their Continental prototypes.

Meanwhile Lawson fought hard to uphold his master

patent monopoly against the encroachments of independent manufacturers, but the rapidly growing industry could not long be held to ransom in this way. The patents became increasingly difficult to uphold until finally they were sold to the Napier Company for the proverbial song in 1907.

Whatever may be said against Lawson's financial ethics it must be conceded that the birth of the English motor industry owed a great deal to his immense energy, his enthusiasm and his remarkable foresight. At a time when the horseless carriage was looked upon as an impracticable toy, Lawson at once realised, and never for a moment doubted, the immense future which lay before the new machine.

Pre-eminent among the English pioneer designers stands the name of F. W. Lanchester. Whereas most of the first English cars to be built were based on continental prototypes, Lanchester's work was entirely original and in many respects it was from the outset in advance of the best Continental practice. Lanchester was works manager and designer to the Forward Gas Engine Company and it was in this way that he became interested in the problem of applying the internal combustion engine to road vehicles. He built his first car in 1895 and it was run on the roads early in 1896, that is to say before the repeal of the " Red Flag " Act. This Lanchester Phaeton, as it was called, can fairly be described as the first full-sized motor-car to be built in England. Powered by a 6 h.p. air-cooled engine having both inlet and exhaust valves mechanically operated, this car was fitted with an epicyclic gearbox with a direct drive on top gear and a live rear axle with worm drive. Wire wheels were fitted and, while other makers for many years continued to use plain bush bearings, Lanchester made extensive use of hardened steel roller bearings from the outset. The modern " self-change " gearbox is the direct descendent of Lanchester's epicyclic gear of 1895, and it is curious that, with the notable exception of the "Model T" Ford, the principle should have lain dormant for so long.

In 1897, Lanchester built his second car, an 8 h.p. two-seater phaeton which was awarded a gold medal at the Richmond Trials of 1899, and which performed with conspicuous success in the 1,000 miles trial of the Automobile Club in the following year. Lanchester paid particular attention to the problem of engine balance, and his horizontally opposed "balanced twin" engine excelled all its contemporaries in smoothness and silence.

As a result of the success of these experimental cars the Lanchester Engine Company was formed in 1899 and a 10 h.p. car was produced at Armourer Works, Montgomery Street, Birmingham. So great was its popularity that in 1903 the works were extended and additional premises taken in Liverpool Street, Birmingham to house the body building and repair departments. With its forward driving position ahead of the engine and its side tiller steering, the 10 h.p. Lanchester was unorthodox both in appearance and design. Yet if we can rid our minds of preconceived notions of what a car should look like, it becomes apparent that the Lanchester was as graceful to look at as it was efficient in performance. When, at a later date, a wide forward mounted radiator took the place of the original leather front apron the elegance of the earliest cars was unfortunately marred.

In the same year that saw the birth of the Lanchester, Herbert Austin was building a small motor tricycle at the Birmingham works of the Wolseley Sheep Shearing Machine Company. He constructed a second three-wheeler in 1897, and in 1900 drove the first production Wolseley car in the 1,000 miles trial, gaining a silver medal. So popular did the Wolseley cars become that, in association with Vickers Sons & Maxim, the Wolseley Tool & Motor Car Company was formed with works at Adderley Park. In 1905 the Wolseley Company entered into association with another pioneer automobilist, J. Davenport Siddeley, and Austin left to establish his own works at Longbridge where the first car was produced under his own name in 1906. The " gate " type change-speed arrangement and the unit construction of engine and gearbox were two important innovations for which Herbert Austin was responsible.

Successful though these early Lanchester and Wolseley cars undoubtedly were, the crippling effect of the " Red Flag " Act was such that English engineers had still a long way to go before they could seriously compete with the French and German manufacturers. The first car to challenge Continental supremacy on its own ground was the product of a successful partnership between S. F. Edge, pioneer driver and astute business man, and Montague Stanley Napier, grandson of the founder of the old established engineering firm of D. Napier & Son of Lambeth, maker of guns, coin weighing machines and weighbridges. Unlike Lawson's engineers, Napier did not make the mistake of underestimating the knowledge and experience which the Continental cars embodied. Where Lanchester was an artist and an original genius, Napier was a fine and painstaking craftsman, with the humility to learn from others. He decided that the best policy was not to expend large sums upon original designs but to take the best available prototype and develop it. Edge bought from Lawson the No. 8 Panhard which had finished second in the Paris-Marseilles race of 1896, and with this car Napier made a number of experiments, finally fitting it with an engine of

his own manufacture. Meanwhile, in 1899, the Motor
Vehicle Company was formed by Edge and Harvey du Cros
to market the cars built " on Panhard lines " by Napier. In
the following year the first 9 h.p. Napier car appeared just
in time to compete in the 1,000 miles trial and was quickly
followed by a 16 h.p. four-cylinder car which caused a great
stir in English motoring circles.

Edge was a firm believer in motor racing both for its
publicity value and as a testing ground for technical developments. In 1900 a 16 h.p. Napier was entered for the
Paris–Toulouse race, and thereafter teams of Napier cars
regularly appeared in the great Continental road races.
Edge's (and Napier's) great achievement came in 1902
when, driving a 40 h.p. Napier, he snatched the coveted
Gordon Bennett Cup from no less a person than that doyen
of French drivers the Chevalier Renee de Knyff of the
Panhard firm. This victory shook the French motor trade
to its foundations and made the Continent aware for the
first time that the English motor industry had become a
force to be reckoned with.

It was largely as a result of the experience gained in the
construction and running of special racing cars that the
first of the famous six-cylinder Napiers was produced
commercially in 1904 and caused a sensation in the trade
both at home and abroad. Three years later, on the newly
opened track at Brooklands, Edge drove his six-cylinder
Napier a distance of 1,581¾ miles in 24 hours, an average
speed of nearly 66 m.p.h. In fact, for the greater part
of the time the car was running at nearly 80 m.p.h.
because Edge was delayed for 1 hr. 40 min. by tyre
troubles. To the general public at this time, such a feat
seemed almost incredible, and it is indicative of the immense strides which had been made in a decade.

Though the Napier car was primarily the product of careful and thoroughly tested design, fine craftsmanship and attention to detail, Napier was not in all things conservative. From the first he relied exclusively on electrical ignition when other makers still looked askance at the new system. He was the first to fit a live rear axle to a high-powered car, and, like Lanchester, he was a pioneer in the use of roller bearings in the transmission. Edge also made his contribution, for it was at his instigation, born of racing experience, that the Napier used for the 24-hour record was fitted with quick-detachable wire wheels.

No mention of the early English pioneers would be complete without the name of Frederick R. Simms. Of English descent but German born, Simms was intimately associated in the earliest horseless carriage days with Herr Gottlieb Daimler. Later, in England, Simms played a leading part in the formation of the Self-Propelled Traffic Association, the Motor Car Club, the Automobile Association and the Society of Motor Manufacturers and Traders (1901) of which he was first President. In 1890, Simms experienced difficulty in obtaining fuel of a sufficiently light specific gravity for some Daimler launch engines which he had imported. He approached the refining firm of Carless, Capel and Leonard who supplied him with suitable fuel. Under the Explosives Act the cans containing this fuel had to be labelled " highly inflammable," and Simms suggested that the fears of customers would be allayed if this refined spirit was called " petrol," from the French *petrole*. The firm accepted the suggestion, used the word as a brand name, and in this way it soon passed into the common currency of English speech.

Simms was also responsible for coining the descriptive term " motor-car " for the new vehicle. This may seem obvious to us, but it was by no means obvious in the days of the horseless carriage and the following names for the new vehicle were suggested in the press : motorfly, automotive, oleolocomotive, volvite, locomotive car, autokenetic, automatic carriage, paramount, electrobat, automobile and autocar. Of all these appellations only the two last named have survived, the former in America and the latter in the title of the well-known motoring journal.

At his works, the Simms Manufacturing Company of Bermondsey and later of Willesden Lane, Simms produced a number of engines and also complete cars. He was the first to construct a multi-cylinder engine with overhead valves all operated mechanically by a single half-speed camshaft. He was also the inventor of the safety bumper which has now become a standard fitting. Simms fitted a set faced with pneumatic rubber cushions to a car as early as 1907, so that it is strange that so many years elapsed before the idea was widely adopted. Simms' greatest contribution to the motor industry, however, was his development, in association with Herr Robert Bosch, of the Simms-Bosch high-tension magneto, and it is in this connection that his name is remembered and perpetuated in the trade.

So rapid was the growth of the motor trade in England after 1900 that it would be impossible in the space of this chapter to mention, let alone trace the development of, the many new vehicles which made their appearance in the Edwardian period. By 1905 it can be said that the first tentative period of experiment was over. While there was still much diversity there had emerged a particular combination of features which were accepted by the majority of manufacturers and by the public and which together gave the motor-car a definitive form of its own which owed nothing to its horse-drawn ancestor.

Once again it was not in England but on the Continent, in Germany in this case, that this definitive form first made its appearance. Though the 1890 Panhard prescribed for the first time the orthodox mechanical layout of engine, clutch, gearbox and transmission it remained a horseless carriage. The 1901 35 h.p. Mercedes with its pressed-steel frame, honeycomb radiator, silent flexible engine and raked steering column has a strong claim to be called the first motor-car in the modern sense of the term. The first " luxury car," the big Mercedes set a new standard which no Edwardian manufacturer either at home or abroad could afford to ignore. From 1901 until the appearance of the first " Silver Ghost " Rolls Royce in 1908, it remained the glass of fashion and the mould of form.

Another landmark in these years which was of almost equal importance was the introduction by Daimler of the Knight double sleeve valve engine. Because of lubrication difficulties at high speeds the Knight engine was artificially choked but set a hitherto unprecedented standard of silence and flexibility within its range. So much so that a number of manufacturers including Mercedes were induced for a time to follow the Daimler fashion. That they set engine designers so high a standard at so early a date was perhaps the greatest contribution of the sleeve valve principle to the evolution of the motor-car. So soon as the poppet valve engine had acquired comparable qualities the complication and inherent technical disadvantages of sleeve valves were no longer justifiable although Daimler and a few other makers remained faithful to them for many years.

The typical medium powered English car of 1905 may be described as follows. The chassis consisted of pressed steel side-members which, following the example of Mercedes, were rapidly superceding the older forms, such as the brazed tubular frames of bicycle type which the Humber Company favoured, straight channel steel members, or wooden beams stiffened with flitch plates. From these side-members the springs were hung, semi-elliptic in front and semi- or three-quarter elliptic in the rear. Wheels were generally of the wooden-spoked artillery type, wire wheels appearing only on *voiturettes* or light tri-cars. On the heavier cars the beaded edge pneumatic tyres were retained on the rims by numerous " security " or " safety " bolts. With non-detachable wheels the removal of a tyre in the event of a puncture was a formidable undertaking even in the garage let alone on a muddy road. For this reason there had appeared the Stepney spare wheel which could be attached to a punctured wheel as a " get-you-home " measure. Soon, however, the Stepney was to disappear as first detachable rims and then detachable wheels became universal. Although a few makers followed the Renault practice of mounting the radiator behind the engine, the forward mounted combined radiator and tank, used in conjunction with circulating pump and fan, as introduced by Mercedes, was now widely adopted. In 1905 these radiators were very similar in appearance and the evolution of distinctive radiator designs by manufacturers was gradual. One of the earliest of these was the finned Daimler radiator which the firm have perpetuated to this day. The champions of the horizontal engine had been outnumbered by 1905, and behind the radiator of our typical Edwardian car was a vertical four-cylinder engine consisting of two cast blocks of two cylinders mounted on a common aluminium crankcase. The cylinder heads were non detachable and of " L " or " T " shape which means to say that the mechanically operated side valves were either actuated by one camshaft or by separate inlet and exhaust camshafts on each side of the crankcase. Bearings were lubricated on the external drip feed principle. Electrical ignition was universal, but either battery and trembler coil or low tension magneto supplied the current and the new Simms-Bosch high-tension magneto was only beginning to make headway. A somewhat crude form of jet carburettor had superseded the old surface type. Prior to 1902, the most usual way of controlling engine speed was by means of an ignition control capable of slowing up the engine by excessive retardation of the spark, a governor being provided against the risk of runaway. Now, however, the practice of regulating engine speed by varying the admission of mixture from the carburettor had become almost universal. To accomplish this some manufacturers had adopted the butterfly throttle valve in the induction pipe which was destined to become universal. Many more relied upon the more complicated method of varying the lift of the inlet valves, and in order to accomplish this on a multi-cylinder engine several highly ingenious mechanical devices were evolved. Despite this change in the method of engine speed control the governor was still a popular device. In its refined form, however, the governor became no longer a safety device but an alternative method of throttle control which enabled the driver to set the throttle in any desired position and allow the governor to take charge. For the thruster this facility had a very limited appeal, but, given a smooth, silent and flexible engine, " cruising on the governor " possessed a peculiar charm which seemed to emphasise such engine qualities and which must be ranked high on the list of the lost pleasures of motoring.

A leather faced cone clutch took the drive from the engine to the separate gearbox. Unless it was propped out of engagement when the car was not in use, and unless the leather face was kept pliant by periodical dressings of colon

Courtesy the Veteran Car Club

PLATE 9

(*above*) *Charles Jarrott and Montague Napier in the first* 12 *h.p. Napier,* 1902*;*
(*below*) *The engine of the first six-cylinder Napier, the first of its type ever built in*
England.

Courtesy A. S. Heal

PLATE 10

(*above*) *Edwardian Voiturette : the 8-10 h.p. Beeston Humberette of* 1905 ; (*below*)
The " Heavy Twenty " Rolls Royce which finished second in the T.T. of 1905. *Percy
Northey at the wheel and behind him the Hon. C. S. Rolls.*

oil, these cone clutches were still apt to be somewhat startling in their action and a few enterprising manufacturers, notably Argyll and Thornycroft, followed the example of Mercedes and were already fitting the multi-plate clutch evolved by Hele-Shaw. As a rule, both engine and gearbox were mounted in a sub-frame to preserve their alignment and prevent damage due to distortion of the main frame. The gearbox was of the orthodox sliding pinion type with quadrant change, though two makes, the Wilson Pilcher and the Rational, followed Lanchester's precedent by using epicyclic gears controlled, in the case of the Rational, by foot pedal and " pre-selector " lever on the steering column.

From the gearbox the drive to the wheels was still commonly taken by chains from a countershaft differential, for Napier's example was not yet widely followed except by the light car makers, and by the firms of Dennis, Thornycroft, Talbot and Humber. The independent hand and foot brakes usually operated an external contracting band-brake behind the gearbox and either expanding or contracting brakes on the rear axle drums. Some makers, instead of using a transmission brake fitted both expanding shoes and contracting bands acting on the same rear drums.

With the old constant-speed type of engine it was desirable, if not essential that the drive should be disconnected when the brakes were applied. Consequently one pedal was arranged to perform both functions, the clutch releasing first and the brakes being brought on by further pressure. The introduction of the throttled engine rendered this device not merely unnecessary but inconvenient and thus the clutch and brake pedals assumed their separate identities. The form of these pedals was also changing, the old "piano type" pedal being rapidly superseded by the modern "push forward" pattern.

Unsatisfactory and short-lived were the "twist-grip" controls for throttle and ignition which some makers provided on the rim of the steering wheel. Apart from the fact that in some moment of sudden crisis the driver might grip the wheel and open the throttle with dire results, the controls changed their position in relation to the driver as the steering wheel was turned.

In 1905, and until 1914, F. W. Lanchester still employed tiller steering on his cars, having carried the principle to a pitch of perfection never achieved by other makers. But the other English manufacturers had all adopted wheel steering and soon Lanchester was to follow suit. The whole steering layout of the early cars had been very crude. The steering mechanism was reversible, that is to say it transmitted road shocks to the tiller and the car tried to "run off" on a cambered road. Furthermore, steering geometry had not been mastered with the result that the front wheels possessed no caster or self-centring action. To hold the car on its course thus called for continuous effort and concentration on the part of the driver, and if we remember the rough state of the roads at this time it becomes easy to appreciate why many serious accidents occurred through the driver losing control of the tiller. The wheel undoubtedly gave the driver more command over errant front wheels, but its introduction was soon followed by an improved steering layout which was light in action, accurate and irreversible, and which held the car to its course without the need for continuous effort.

Though a few makers clung to archaic features such as automatic inlet valves and even solid or "cushion" tyres, others introduced designs which pointed towards the future. Among the latter, Continental importers were still to the fore. Thus both Delaunay Belleville and De Dion used the modern type of pressure lubrication for main and big end bearings through a drilled crankshaft. The Moto-bloc engine and gearbox were built as one unit, while the Pipe car was fitted with push rod operated overhead valves inclined at 45 deg., an arrangement which made possible a hemi-spherical combustion chamber of modern type. But the English manufacturers were not far behind. Maudslay featured an overhead camshaft operating vertical valves, Belsize were using push-rod operated overhead valves, while several makers including Napier fitted overhead inlet valves in conjunction with side exhaust valves. The four cylinders of the Ariel car were cast in one block although four separate detachable heads were fitted.

Now that we have surveyed the engine and chassis of the typical Edwardian car of 1905 we are free to examine the bodywork and accessories with which these chassis were adorned. The older types of body, " Dogcart," " Phaeton " or " Landau," directly derived in design as in name from horse-drawn prototypes, were now rapidly dying out in favour of more specialised coachwork. The most popular of these was an open four-seater which was known as a " side entrance " body to distinguish it from the older type with rear entrance which decanted the passenger into the middle of the road. The over-all height of the body was considerable. Not only did the straight, overslung chassis dictate a high centre of gravity, but the body placed on top of it had to conform with prevailing fashion. The low " lounge chair," symbol of modern laxity, has dictated the design of our car seating but would by no means have been suited to Edwardian manners. Our fathers preferred to sit upright, thighs horizontal and forelegs parallel with the spine. Moreover, the Edwardian driver wisely decided that he must look down upon, and not along, the bonnet of his car, while the rear seats were often mounted higher still to give the rear passengers an uninterrupted view of the road ahead. A straight across seat was usually provided at the rear, but the front seats were of the bucket type although they were fixed and formed an integral part of the body.

Here was no streamlined shape, no stark unbroken surface of sheet metal. For although the motor-car had ceased to be a horseless carriage its bodywork still reflected the tradition of the craftsman coachbuilder in its opulent curves, in its massive solidity and fine workmanship and in the elegant lining and beading of its resplendent coach finish. Instead of a straight waistline the body sides swept up to the height of the seat backs in a series of bold reverse curves from the floor level, for no doors were fitted to the driving compartment. The flat section rear mudguards followed the same bold curves as they covered, not only the rear wheels but also the driving chain sprockets on the countershaft. The low flat bonnet terminated abruptly in a high vertical scuttle, upon the rear side of which any instruments were mounted.

To the richness of coach finish and leather upholstery liberally studded with buttons was added the glitter of polished brass ; brass radiator ; brass tube encasing the tall steering column ; brass sight-feed lubricator or oil pump on the mahogany scuttle. An elaborate brass bulb horn and large brass lamps set the final seal of baroque magnificence on the whole equipage. From a rubber bulb placed conveniently near the driver's hand a flexible tube curved away either to a straight trumpet shaped in the semblance of a serpent with wide open jaws or to an instrument with the intricate convolutions of a cornet. Such a horn emitted no peremptory or vulgar toot but a deep note, sonorous and prolonged, imperious yet dignified. Steam cars, on the other hand, commonly favoured a bell until that form of warning was monopolised by ambulances and fire-engines.

When, a few years later, heavy commercial vehicles began to roar and rumble along the main roads on their solid tyres the private motorist soon discovered that a much more strident noise was necessary in order to reach the ears of the lorry driver who seldom or never was equipped with a mirror and who could not, in any event, see anything behind him but his own dust. For such emergency use a piercing exhaust whistle or a hand-operated Klaxon which emitted a raucous bark soon became popular. In the absence of such equipment various emergency measures such as shouting or blowing whistles were resorted to. I can remember as a small child being armed against this contingency by my father with a whistle with rotary vanes which emitted a sound like that produced by an air raid siren and with which I delighted to disturb road monopolising lorries. The hand Klaxon was soon electrified, and after the first war the old decorous bulb horn was widely replaced by a variety of ear-offending electric instruments of the diaphragm type. The modern tendency to supersede these hideous noises by means of " wind-tone " horns is highly commendable.

The lighting system in vogue in 1905 usually consisted of oil burning rear and side lamps,[1] the latter mounted on the scuttle, and an acetylene gas headlamp or lamps supplied from a separate generator by rubber tubing. The Motor

[1]Veteran Car owners who experience trouble with these old oil lamps should remember that they were designed to burn colza oil and not paraffin.

Car Act of 1902, however, which established the present system of car registration and number plates, posed a problem when it stipulated that the rear number plate must be fully illuminated at night. The average oil rear lamp gave insufficient light to comply with the law, while a gas light with its small burner and long length of tubing was apt to go out. Thus, while the night driving motorist paid dearly in fines, the possibility of electric lighting for cars was eagerly discussed. The difficulty was that no one had so far evolved an electric bulb with a filament which could withstand the vibration of a moving vehicle.

The motorist of 1905 was prejudiced, not without reason, against a windscreen of plate glass. On touring cars a voluminous cape-cart hood might be provided, but no windscreen. Even on the few cars with closed coachwork windscreens were seldom fitted. The rear compartment might be totally enclosed by means of a division, but with rare exceptions only a roof extended and supported by stanchions protected the driving seats. Thus in the typical car of 1905 driver and passenger were as exposed to the elements as they had been in the horseless carriage of 1896. With the exception of the peaked cap, the smart autocarist's uniform evolved by Lawson was therefore of little value except on ceremonial occasions, the rigours of the English climate demanding apparel of far heavier quality. Of these garments the hairy goat-skin coat, or *peau de bique* was for many years considered the height of motoring fashion. The Chevalier Renee de Knyff had originally appeared in one when he drove in the Paris–Marseilles race in 1896, and thenceforth it became *de rigueur* for enterprising automobilists. The massive figure of de Knyff was in any circumstances sufficiently formidable to intimidate his more nervous opponents, but when he donned his *peau de bique* the effect must have been positively awe inspiring. For it would be difficult to distinguish the point where the Chevalier's flowing beard ended and the goat-skin began, and easy to imagine that Bellarius of *Cymbeline* had left his cave to don leather helmet and goggles. But when the bulky goatskin was worn in conjunction with one of Lawson's caps by the driver of a diminutive tricar the effect achieved was anything but impressive.

Even in days of high summer when the goatskin could safely be left to the moths, no motorist would dare to venture upon a run of any distance without donning a long white dustcoat reaching almost to the ankles. Similar coats were worn by his lady friends with the addition of heavy veils tied under the chin, which performed the dual function of protecting their faces and holding on their large hats. For the white roads of England had not yet been covered by a funereal coating of tarmac or bitumen, and the passage of any motor vehicle raised a dense column of choking and blinding dust which hung long in still summer air before settling like flour on banks and hedgerows. This dust problem was the subject of much attention, and while it was appreciated that a dustless road surface was the ultimate solution, various dust-laying mixtures were evolved which could be sprayed on to the road surface by water carts. Road racing circuits or the roads in the vicinity of outdoor sporting events were often treated in this way.

For the same reason the motorist would welcome a light shower, but more prolonged rainfall would, by converting the dust into mud of the consistency of cream, produce an alternative that was equally unpleasant. When we remember that the cars using these loose or greasy surfaces possessed narrow tyres, a high centre of gravity and ineffective rear wheel brakes it is easy to understand why a little miscalcu-

lation or over-exuberance was apt to produce skids of terrifying magnitude and often disastrous result. How to overcome or minimise " the dreaded side-slip," as it was then
called, was a burning question among motorists of the
Edwardian era. Commercial solutions varied from grips
which could be attached to the wheels (ancestors of the
modern snow-chains) to numerous patterns of tyre tread
for which great claims were made. One of these, which
enjoyed a great vogue for a time, consisted of a leather band
set with steel studs which was vulcanised on to the casing.
On certain surfaces these steel studded tyres fulfilled their
purpose fairly well, but on others, notably granite setts, they
tended to increase rather than diminish the hazard of a side-
slip.

In one respect many motorists depended upon a rough
road surface. The " wrap-on " type of external contracting
band brake fitted to many early cars was only effective in a
forward direction. This meant that the car tended to run
back if it stopped, voluntarily or involuntarily, when
ascending a steep hill. The crude cure for this was a steel
bar with a chisel point known as a " sprag " which hung
below the chassis and could be lowered by the driver in
case of need. The chisel point then bit into the road surface
and so propped the car up. As I found by experience with
my 1903 Humber, the sprag was not to be depended upon
on a smooth modern road surface. This fact once saved me
a summons for carrying a passenger in the car on Trade
Plates on a Sunday. The arm of the law eventually retired
baffled and defeated in the face of a technical discourse on
the inadequacy of sprags in the modern world and the consequent need for a nimble passenger in the event of emergency. It is, perhaps, just as well that the coming of smooth
road surfaces coincided with the introduction of brakes

which made sprags a " by-gone." The ultimate refinement of the sprag, however, was independent of the road surface for it consisted of a ratchet and pawl device on the propeller shaft, the ratchet teeth being commonly cut on the periphery of the transmission brake drum. This arrangement was provided not so much to assist inadequate brakes as to facilitate starting from rest on a steep gradient, a function which it performed admirably. In fact such a contrivance would be an asset today, particularly on cars fitted with ill contrived " pistol grip " handbrakes.

The typical English car of 1905 or 1906 was a reliable and vastly improved machine compared with the horseless carriages of the '90s, but it still failed to surpass the best achievements of the Continental manufacturers. Though the six-cylinder Napier also vaunted the title, the German Mercedes boasted proudly and not without reason that it was " The Best Car in the World." But in 1907 the tables were turned by the most important event in the history of the motor industry. This was the appearance of the first Rolls Royce " Silver Ghost." The Rolls Royce set the world a new standard of excellence which has never been surpassed and its claim to the title of " The Best Car in the World " eventually proved indisputable.

Like so many of the outstanding developments of the Industrial Revolution, the Rolls Royce car was the fruit of an association between a self-taught and a self-made practical genius and a well-educated and highly cultured man with outstanding business ability. In this case Henry Royce was the James Watt of the partnership while Claude Johnson played the part of Matthew Boulton. The enthusiasm of the Honourable C. S. Rolls also made a contribution to the success of the enterprise which might have been even greater but for his untimely death in a flying accident.

Henry Royce was the son of James Royce, an unsuccessful miller, and he was born at Alwalton Mill on the River Nene in 1863. At the age of fourteen he went as an apprentice to the Great Northern Railway locomotive shops at Peterborough. By so doing Royce became familiar with one of the finest examples of the locomotive builder's craft—the famous 8 ft. single drivers of Patrick Stirling. Thus it would not be too fanciful to attribute to Stirling's example the quality of beauty allied with mechanical excellence which characterised all Henry Royce's workmanship.

His apprenticeship concluded, Royce tramped the country in search of work, obtaining vicarious employment in Leeds, London and Liverpool before, in 1884 he set up a small electrical business of his own in Cooke Street, Manchester which ultimately became the firm of Royce Ltd., makers of dynamos, motors and electric cranes.

It was at Manchester in 1904 that Henry Royce built his first 10 h.p. two-cylinder car. In the autumn of that year the excellence of this car attracted the attention of Claude Johnson and the Honourable C. S. Rolls, partners in the firm of C. S. Rolls & Co., automobile concessionaires of London. As a result, Rolls & Co., undertook to sell Royce's entire output of cars while Royce in his turn agreed to supply them with 15 h.p. three-cylinder, 20 h.p. four-cylinder and 30 h.p. six-cylinder cars in addition to the small two-cylinder model. These larger cars fulfilled the promise of their small predecessor and in 1905 one of the 20 h.p. cars, which became known as " The Heavy Twenties " or " Grey Ghosts," finished second in the Tourist Trophy race in the hands of Percy Northey. Successful though this car was, it was rapidly superseded by the improved " Light Twenty " which C. S. Rolls drove to victory in the T.T. of 1906. Yet even this car failed to satisfy the exacting standard of excellence which Henry Royce had set himself, and thus it was that the prototype 40/50 h.p. " Silver Ghost " emerged from the Manchester works in 1907.

Even today, to handle one of these early " Silver Ghosts " is a revelation, such is its mechanical excellence and effortless performance, and the impression which the car made upon the motorist of 1907 can be well imagined. So convinced were Rolls and Johnson that a great future lay before the " Silver Ghost " that they urged Henry Royce to drop the manufacture of all previous models. Already the new Rolls Royce Company had been formed with works at Derby and here, in 1908, manufacture of the " Silver Ghost " began. It was a bold move indeed to rely exclusively on the production of so large and costly a vehicle and it remains to this day without successful precedent in the motor industry. Such few manufacturers who have produced vehicles in any way comparable with the Rolls Royce have either failed or they have continued to depend financially on their output of cars of more modest size and price. But the confidence of Rolls and Johnson in the product of Royce's genius was fully justified by the result, more fully, perhaps, than even they had dreamed. Though it was the subject of continuous detail improvement, the " Silver Ghost " chassis remained in production at Derby until 1924 when it was at last superseded by the " New Phantom." Eighteen years continuous production of one model is in itself a record which was only approached, curiously enough, by a car which was at the opposite pole to the Rolls Royce. This was the famous American " Model T " Ford which lived from 1912 to 1926.

It would be safe to say without exaggeration that the " Silver Ghost " was not only the best car ever built, but that it was the finest mechanical engineering achievement of the Edwardian era. It was more than a commercial success; it made the name of its makers a household synonym for excellence the world over, a testimonial without parallel in history. What was the secret of this outstanding success ? Having once carried out an extensive overhaul of a 1911 " Silver Ghost," I have my answer to this question. It is simple but it is unpopular and disregarded in this year of grace 1950. The " Silver Ghost " was not an inspired and original invention but a product of consummate craftsmanship. The genius of Henry Royce lay in his ability to select all that was best in the automobile engineering practice of the period and then to improve and develop his selections until they satisfied his exacting standard. That standard was simply the best that could be achieved and, like every true craftsman the world over, he would not be diverted from it by any specious argument of commercial expediency. He demanded the utmost excellence in both materials and workmanship, and the fact that these demands were so magnificently met by all those who worked under him to produce the " Silver Ghost " was due to the inspiration of Royce's example. For Royce was no specialist designer who, to use the disgruntled fitter's phrase, " tightened nuts with a pencil " ; on the contrary he was a versatile craftsman in the fullest and most practical sense. It is recounted of him that often in the early days he was to be found working at the fitter's bench or at the controls of a machine tool if some practical problem had arisen or if he was dissatisfied with the way in which a job was being done.

We are often inclined to give too much credit for architectural or engineering achievements to the designers and too little to the practical executants, but in this case it can truly be said that Henry Royce built the " Silver Ghost."

The smallest component of the chassis, in its workmanship, finish and fitness for its purpose, reveals his meticulous care. The same quality is manifest in the sweet and precise " feel " of all the controls of the car from the gear lever to the small ignition switch in the centre of the steering column

Another lesson which the " Silver Ghost " teaches, and which is widely forgotten or ignored in this age of mass production when quantity is the goal, is the true economy of quality. Owing to the fallacious idea that quality is a luxury for the rich, the product of the craftsman tends to be frowned upon by our modern demagogues. The first cost of the Rolls Royce was certainly high, but in the value it gave for this initial outlay it was probably the cheapest car ever made. This economy was demonstrated by the prototype " Silver Ghost " when Claude Johnson entered it for a 15,000 miles test under the observation of the Royal Automobile Club. Night and day the car ran continuously between London and Glasgow, the total cost in petrol, oil, tyres and repairs working out at 4½d. per mile. When the test had been completed the car was overhauled under observation in order to make it equal to new and the total cost of the necessary replacements amounted to £2 2s. 7d. Again, in 1911, a " Silver Ghost " ran from London to Edinburgh in top gear and recorded a petrol consumption of 24 m.p.g.—a truly astonishing figure for so large a car. Meanwhile the original prototype " Silver Ghost " of the 15,000 miles trial passed into private ownership and was still running in 1925 having covered a further 350,000 miles.[1] It was the introduction of the high horse-power tax based on an arbitrary formula calculated on cylinder bore

---

[1]It is gratifying to record the fact that this car is still in existence and has just been meticulously restored by Mr. Stanley Sears. *See frontispiece.*

which made the Rolls Royce exclusively a rich man's car and has tended to obscure its true economy.

The outbreak of the first world war in August, 1914, rather than the death of Edward VII in 1910 marked the end of an epoch in our social history. Consequently it has become fashionable today to describe any car built prior to 1915 as " Edwardian." As in World War II, the evolution of the motor-car became suspended between 1914 and 1920 while manufacturers concentrated on war production and the subsequent changeover from war to peace. Between 1910 and the outbreak of war, on the other hand, development was very rapid. Improvements in foundry and machine shop practice led to the widespread appearance of light and compact high-speed " monobloc " engines, many of them employing overhead valves and all fitted with high-tension magnetos and pressure lubrication. Automatic or variable lift valves disappeared. Many makers adopted unit construction of engine and gearbox. The latter often provided four speeds, and the right-hand gate change-speed arrangement became standard practice in place of the old quadrant type. Live axles became universal except in the case of small cycle-cars and heavy commercial vehicles. Manufacturers evolved distinctive radiator designs many of which continued to characterise their productions until the end of the '20s. The prejudice against glass windscreens was overcome, while the introduction of the tungsten filament lamp led to the widespread use of electric lighting sets in place of acetylene or oil. Nevertheless, few makers appear to have realised the possibilities of the new lighting system, for the majority introduced it as an " optional extra " on their cars. Instead of incorporating a positively driven dynamo in their design, a dynamo was hung on by an improvised bracket and driven by a leather linked

" whittle " belt from the engine or, more commonly, from the transmission. Many were the broken whittle belts which bestrewed the roads of England at this time, and contemporary motorists still flinch at the mere mention of their name. The most conservative among them will agree that the modern endless rubber " Vee " belt is infinitely superior.

The Brolt electric starter, with its ingenious method of inertia engagement known today as the Bendix drive, also made its appearance at this time, though it was not very widely adopted. Instead, some ingenious methods of mechanical starting from the driving seat made their appearance. In one of these the engine could be rotated by pulling the gear lever. In order to achieve this feat the lever was moved into a slot beside the gate in which position it engaged the starting mechanism and became disengaged from the gear selector shafts.

Much attention was paid by designers to chassis improvement. Frames not only became longer and stiffer but lower as side members were upswept over axles and springs became flatter. No longer need the bodies fitted to such chassis be built to withstand the fierce stresses imposed by the older, more flexible frames. The old massive style of coachwork with its baroque curves disappeared and with it went the last suggestion of the horseless carriage. In its place the coachbuilder evolved a pure motor-car style longer, lower and rectilinear, its more severe outline being offset to some extent by the introduction of the domed, mudguards which rapidly superseded the old flat type.

As a result of these developments the four-seater touring car of 1914 with its straight-sided " torpedo " body, its high bonnet, distinctive radiator, continuous running boards, electric lamps and detachable wheels of stud or

Rudge " knock-off " type was decidedly " modern " in appearance. It was, in fact, much more closely akin to the cars of the 1920s than to the true Edwardian car built during the lifetime of Edward VII.

The most advanced cars of the period immediately preceding the outbreak of war, many of them the products of firms new to the industry, had little chance to achieve popularity until after the war was over. Because their reputations were made on the roads of the '20s they may be regarded as post-war designs and considered in the following chapter.

PLATE 11

(*above*) *A characteristic example of Edwardian closed coachwork ;* (*below*) *A typical Edwardian touring scene ; taken at Ewell en route for the Derby,* 1909

Courtesy A. S. Heal

PLATE 12

THE " HORSELESS CARRIAGE " BECOMES THE MOTOR-CAR

(*above*) *An Edwardian Daimler with typical " side-entrance " touring body ; (below)
A* 1914 12-16 *h.p. Sunbeam with " torpedo " touring body. Note electric lighting
system.*

PLATE 13

*(above) The typical light car of the early '20s : the 11 h.p. Calcott ; (below) Light
car refinement in the '20s : the six-cylinder A.C. drop-head coupé.*

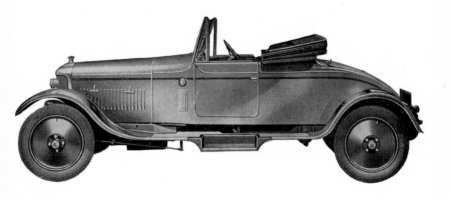

PLATE 14

TYPICAL CARS OF THE ' 20s

(*above*) *The medium powered tourer : the* 1924 *Austin* 12/4 *; (below) The cycle-car :
the* 1920 *twin-cylinder air-cooled G.N.*

CHAPTER FIVE

THE ROARING TWENTIES

THE MOTORIST in this country has been the victim of an ever-increasing burden of taxation. Under the Locomotives on Highways Act of 1896 every four-wheeled car not exceeding 2 tons in weight paid a total annual tax of £4 4s. to which the Motor Car Act of 1903 added a registration fee of £1. On 1st January, 1910, taxation on horse-power based on R.A.C. formula was introduced, the original rates being : up to 6½ h.p.—2 gns. ; 12. h.p.—3 gns. ; 16 h.p.—4 gns. ; 26 h.p.—6 gns. ; 33 h.p.—8 gns. ; 40 h.p.—10 gns. ; 60 h.p.—£21. At the same time there was a petrol tax of 3d. per gallon which was doubled during the war years. On 1st January, 1921 the annual tax was raised to £1 per h.p., while the petrol tax was repealed, only to be imposed again in 1928 at 4d. per gallon and doubled in 1931.

These taxes had a profound effect upon English car design. Without the taxation factor to consider the designer's problem would have been more straightforward. He would have aimed to produce an internal combustion engine which would emulate the characteristics of the steam engine ; which would, that is to say, combine a good torque at low speed with smoothness, silence and flexibility. A long stroke would satisfy the first requirement, but not the second, while piston speed at the higher revolutions would be dangerously high. A short stroke, on the other hand, would produce the requisite silence and smoothness but would not give good low speed torque and so necessitate much use of the gears. For the touring car undoubtedly the best compromise was the " square " engine of large bore and moderate stroke. Edwardian designers were heading in this direction, and the " Silver Ghost " Rolls Royce engine was the supreme example of what the " square " engine could achieve. But the introduction of taxation on a horse-power basis calculated on cylinder bore instead of on volume, or cubic capacity as it is usually called, effectually killed the " square " engine in this country outside the luxury class. In its place designers produced " tax dodging " engines in which a small bore was combined with a very long stroke, and only the limiting factor of piston speed prevented this practice being carried to fantastic lengths.

Though there were already a number of light cars and cycle-cars on the market to tempt the impecunious would-be motorist, the most popular vehicle before the first world war had been a medium powered car of from 15 to 20 h.p. It was the raising of the tax to £1 per h.p. in 1921 which caused the light car boom and reduced the numbers of cars of over 12 h.p. on the English roads to a minority. Although this diversion of logical evolution by taxation is to be regretted, it undoubtedly stimulated metallurgical and technical development by setting designers the problem of obtaining the maximum amount of power from the smallest practicable engine unit. How far and how quickly they succeeded is revealed by the fact that, to quote only two examples, the 1½-litre push-rod o.h.v. Alvis engine of 1923 was capable of producing 50 b.h.p. at 4,500 r.p.m., while the famous 1½-litre side valve Anzani engine of the same year, which was used in many light cars of the '20s, produced nearly 40 b.h.p., at 3,600 r.p.m. in standard form. Moreover, it should be emphasised that these small engines were by no means specially prepared or highly tuned units liable to sudden and catastrophic disintegration but standard products which gave years of reliable service.

Of the many light cars which appeared in the great light car boom in the early '20s a number enjoyed only an ephemeral existence and then vanished forever despite the fact that they by no means lacked merit. Forgotten by the younger generation of motorists, such names as Bayliss-Thomas, Crouch, Rhode, Deemster, Calthorpe, Calcott, Gwynne, Albert, Horstmann, Hampton, Palladium and Eric Campbell can still evoke nostalgic memories for those who remember the roads of the '20s. One of these ephemerals which enjoyed a tremendous vogue was the Wolverhampton built Clyno which in its heyday could be seen on the roads to an extent only surpassed by the Model T Ford and the " bull-nosed " Morris, that most successful and long-lived product of the boom years. But Wolverhampton seems fated to be the home of lost causes where the manufacture of private cars is concerned, and in their premature efforts at quantity production the Clyno Company overreached themselves, sacrificed the quality of their earlier cars, and vanished from the scene.

Other light cars of this period, though their names vanished, lived on in a new guise. Perhaps the best example of this class was the " Wolseley 10 " with its small four-cylinder overhead camshaft engine. From this first Wolseley 10, the Morris Minor, Wolseley Hornet and M.G. Midget all stemmed.

Some of these light cars were primarily sporting vehicles and will be dealt with in a later chapter, while of the remaining successful makes which appeared in the immediate post-war period it is difficult to single out individual cars without risking the accusation of personal partiality or prejudice. Nevertheless I consider that the A.C. merits a special mention.

In 1912 the redoubtable S. F. Edge had sold out his interest in the Napier concern and agreed with Napier that he would not engage in the motor trade for a period of seven years. On the expiry of that period Edge became associated with Autocarriers Limited. Before the war this firm had built the little three-wheeled A.C. Sociable which, though of weird appearance, earned a good reputation for reliability. The first-four-wheeled A.C. of 10 h.p. appeared in 1916 but under Edge's aegis the Company was re-formed and produced two new models, a four-cylinder car powered by a 1½-litre Anzani engine in 1920, and a 2-litre six-cylinder car of 16 rated h.p. in 1922. Both these cars earned a great reputation, but it is the latter which particularly concerns us here. It was the aim of the designers of the A.C. six to produce a light car with a performance which, in its quality of smoothness and silence, would be comparable with that of a luxury car of high horse-power. In this, so far as the engine was concerned, they certainly succeeded for the six-cylinder A.C. of 1922 was years ahead of its time and was almost as revolutionary as the six-cylinder Napier of 1904. With the exception of the cylinder head, the engine was constructed almost entirely of aluminium, " wet " steel liners being fitted in an alloy cylinder block. The valves were operated by a single overhead camshaft and the magneto and dynamo were driven by opposed right-angle skew gears. The result was a remarkably light, flexible, silent and compact power unit which, like all really sound designs, stood the test of time. Though subject to detail modifications, the same basic design has continued in production until the present day, a truly remarkable span of twenty-nine years. With its silent and effortless top gear performance the A.C. six merited its title of " the Rolls Royce of light cars." Fortunately, the flexibility of the engine and the lightness of the car ensured a remarkable range in top gear, for when a change had to be made to the indirect gears loud tram-like noises were heard and any Rolls Royce comparison became odious. For Edge clung obstinately to a singularly noisy and unpleasant three-speed gearbox which was incorporated in the back axle and which included a curious disc brake mounted at the rear of the axle casing. This gearbox, which was fitted to both four and six-cylinder models, marred an otherwise outstanding car. It was finally dropped when the chassis was entirely redesigned in 1933.

Although primarily built as a touring car, Edge was as great a believer in the value of competition work as he had been in his Napier days and he entered A.C.s with success for a number of competitions, races and record attempts. Driven by J. A. Joyce at Brooklands, a four-cylinder A.C. was the first 1½-litre car to cover a hundred miles in the hour, while in 1924 a 2-litre car driven by T. Gillett broke the 24-hours world's class record with a speed of 82.59 m.p.h

The two-seater drop-head coupé body fitted to the A.C. six of this period was an outstandingly comfortable, convenient and well-built example of light car coachwork in its day. One curious feature which I recall was that the filler of the scuttle petrol tank protruded through the dashboard. When I once had the misfortune to turn one of these cars over as a result of a steering failure and found petrol pouring on to me through the filler cap I came to the conclusion that this was not a good idea and thanked my stars that I was not smoking at the time.

Though every light car of this period possessed certain individual features of this sort which gave to each make a very definite character, they may be described as infinite variations within an accepted convention, and radical departures from this convention such as the G.W.K. with its multi-variable friction drive (which worked well in dry weather) were the exception rather than the rule. The majority were content to follow an orthodox layout of engine, gearbox and final drive which had been established before the war. Many makers, in fact, shared the same proprietory engine unit, Anzani, Ruby, Dorman or White & Poppe.

Such orthodoxy, however, by no means applied to the cycle-car, and it was in this field that aspiring inventors really ran riot, achieving freaks of fancy which recalled the earliest formative years of the horseless carriage. They offered the impecunious motorist machines which enabled him to re-enact the adventures of the first pioneers. For to essay a journey of a hundred miles or more in one of the more spidery cycle-cars of 1920 was to challenge fate, and before the journey was over the driver could rely upon experiencing every shade of emotion from delight through apprehension to frustration, fury and despair. There was plenty of choice in this field. There was the Tamplin or the Richardson or the diminutive Carden with its two-stroke engine at the rear. There was the A.V. monocar which resembled an animated Minimax fire-extinguisher mounted on thin disc wheels like black japanned tea trays. Like the ancient Benz, the A.V. was started by pulling a string at the rear and it probably possessed less road-holding ability than any car ever built. There was the Bleriot-Whippet with its variable speed belt drive which, like the G.W.K. friction discs, resented wet weather. Motoring through pouring rain in a cycle-car with inadequate weather protection was never conducive to high spirits, but to this pervasive damping the slipping belt of the Bleriot provided just that last malicious stroke of misfortune calculated to plunge the driver into the depths of morose despondency.

By far the most famous and successful of the lighter and unorthodox types of cycle-car was the G.N. evolved by Messrs. H. R. Godfrey and A. Frazer-Nash when they were apprentices in the steam-engine firm of Willans & Robinson of Rugby. It was born before the 1914 war as a belt driven machine and had already made a reputation by the time the war broke out. But it was the post-war chain driven machine with twin-cylinder air-cooled engine which achieved tremendous popularity and success in competition. No one familiar with the G.N. can escape the conclusion that what I can only describe as an element of inspired good luck contributed largely to this success. Where many carefully evolved and costly designs failed or achieved only limited success, the G. N. triumphed by the simplest and crudest means. The chassis resembled a bedstead frame and violated every structural canon in its lack of bracing. It consisted merely of a quadrangle of straight channel steel with four short quarter-elliptic springs clamped on by U-bolts at the corners. Another U-bolt clamped on the steering box. The same crudity informed the whole machine from the big twin engine at the front to the rear transmission with its four whirling chains, sprockets, countershaft and sliding dogs all exposed to the view save for an undertray which conveniently retained in a sticky compound of grease and gear oil any part of the mechanism which disintegrated. Yet I can testify from personal experience that this heretical design amply justified itself, for the first car I ever owned was a 1922 G. N. " Popular " model which I acquired for the large sum of £6 in 1929. I liked it so well that I acquired a second car of the same date and type which I ran continuously until 1935 when its long career was only terminated by an unfortunate accident which reduced it to tangled scrap iron.

Despite its crudity the G.N. was remarkable for its good road holding and accurate steering. Moreover the unorthodox transmission was almost entirely trouble free save for very occasional chain breakage through failure to maintain correct adjustment, and it gave a very quick and easy gear change. These factors, combined with an excellent driving position giving good visibility and ample leg room for the tallest driver made it the least tiring of cars to drive. It was certainly distressingly noisy, but when the two large cylinders were consorting well with one another and got down to their job in earnest the sensation was altogether different from and more gratifying than the tiresome buzz of the small four or six-cylinder car. This does not mean to say that G. N. motoring lacked excitement. On more than one occasion fire broke out under the bonnet of my car, while wheels had a disconcerting habit of flying off if the hub caps were not carefully checked from time to time. The G.N. lived on under another name—Frazer-Nash —but consideration of this car properly belongs to another chapter.

Apart from the four-wheeled cycle-cars, the 1920s saw many three-wheelers appear on the roads. Of these, cars such as the T.B. or the Castle Three enjoyed only a brief vogue and were soon forgotten, for the Morgan has always been supreme in this class and its position has only been seriously challenged once, in the early '30s by the three-wheeled B.S.A. The first Morgan three-wheeler appeared as early as 1910, and from the first its design included tubular backbone chassis construction and independent front wheel suspension, features of immense significance which were not appreciated by English designers until the 1930s despite the Italian example of the Lancia Lambda.

In a class above the smaller and more spidery cycle-cars were those which were virtually orthodox light cars except for the fact that they fitted twin-cylinder engines built on motor-cycle lines. Of these the Rover " 8 " and the Jowett proved the most popular while other examples were the A.B.C. and the Belsize Bradshaw. It is perhaps a little unfair to class the Jowett as a cycle-car. Its flat twin water-cooled engine, first evolved in 1910, was as smooth and flexible as a small four and possessed better low-speed torque. In every other respect it was an orthodox light car and its sturdy merit enabled it to survive the eclipse of its contemporaries. It continued in production until 1939[1] and is the parent of the present " flat-four " Jowett.

The Belsize Bradshaw was another and less successful attempt to produce a twin-cylinder car with the refinement of a small four. The two-cylinder Bradshaw engine inclined at 90 deg., was beautifully made. It was described as " oil cooled " because the cylinder barrels were enveloped in an enormous aluminium crankcase casting. The amount of cooling they thus received is problematical, but the principle certainly had a sound-damping effect. A vaned flywheel mounted in front of the engine and an aluminium cowling forced air over the finned alloy heads. I once owned one of these cars. It was silent, comfortable and reliable but the suspension was too soft, while it lacked the character and performance of the cruder but more virile G.N. One strange little characteristic of my Belsize was

[1]The current Jowett " Bradford " van is still powered by the flat twin engine. This power unit therefore has had an amazing production run of no less than forty years.

that on sudden braking, or when descending a steep hill the self-starter pinion used to run forward and chink against the flywheel, producing, to the surprise of my passengers, a loud sound like the ringing of a school bell.

The Rover " 8 " with its flat twin air-cooled engine was cruder and noisier than either the Belsize or the Jowett but its dogged reliability made it deservedly popular and I know of one example which is in regular use on the road at the time of writing. By contrast with this trio which were essentially utilitarian, the A.B.C. with its handsome and rakish-looking body of polished aluminium was unquestionably a sporting machine. It was powered by an air-cooled flat twin engine with push-rod operated overhead valves. It followed contemporary aircraft practice by using steel cylinders machined from the solid, and, like the Belsize engine, it was designed by Granville Bradshaw. The little car was a very lively performer but it was unfortunately marred by an unsatisfactory valve gear which shed push-rods with maddening frequency. Also, like the G.N., it had a tendency to catch fire which was particularly unfortunate because the petrol tank was mounted directly above the engine. One most misguided piece of ingenuity on the part of the A.B.C. designer was the idea of using the cap of the elaborate dummy radiator as a petrol tank filler. Many were the luckless A.B.C. owners who had their petrol tanks topped up with water by thoughtful garage hands.

The light car came to stay but the cycle-car enjoyed only a brief heyday. It was doomed from the day in 1922 when Lord Austin first astonished the motoring public with the famous Austin Seven. This miniature car soon banished the cyclecar from the roads and was quickly followed by others ; by the Morris Minor, the Triumph Seven and the Ford Eight. Attempts to stage a revival of the cyclecar type such as the rear-engined Rover " Scarab " failed miserably.

Though the spate of light cars and cycle-cars dominates the motoring history of the early '20s, there was also great activity in the production of slightly larger cars between the heavy " twelve-four " type and 16 h.p. Here again one can recall the appearance of many vanished makes, the majority of which possessed merit ; Argyll, product of a pioneer Scottish firm who were the first in Britain to introduce front-wheel brakes ; Arrol Johnston ; Angus Sanderson ; Cubitt ; Star ; Dawson ; Bean ; Belsize ; Ruston-Hornsby and many more. But when the first post-war boom was over many of these names disappeared forever, for only the larger and most securely established concerns, often producing more than one model, weathered the strikes and economic blizzards which marked the latter years of the decade. The Wolseley, the Humber, the Austin and Rover " 12/4s " ; the Hillman and Standard fourteens ; the Morris Oxford ; and, in a somewhat higher category, the 16 h.p. Sunbeam, all these established themselves securely in public favour.

Owing to high taxation and the increased cost of living the small demand for high-horse-powered cars did not encourage many newcomers to this field. The market was mainly held by old-established firms who produced in addition cars of smaller horse-power. Even firms which had built their reputation on large cars were forced to produce smaller models or abandon car manufacture. Daimler maintained production of their magnificent " Silent Knight " sleeve valve cars though they introduced smaller models. Lanchester dropped their 30 h.p. car and ultimately pooled their resources with Daimler and concentrated on small and medium-powered models. Napier

launched on the post-war market a superb 40/50 h.p.
" Torpedo " model with overhead camshaft engine, but
the firm soon gave up car production altogether and concentrated on aero-engine development. The big Sunbeam
held its own throughout the decade with the support of
the smaller models. Even Rolls Royce bowed to the storm
to the extent of producing a 20 h.p. car although the position
of the Silver Ghost and the later Phantom proved unassailable.

The fortunes of those who were so bold as to invade the
luxury market in the '20s make melancholy reading. There
was the ephemeral Sizaire-Berwick which, in external
appearance, resembled a Rolls Royce all too closely. There
was the fabulous Leyland Straight-Eight designed by
Parry Thomas. The Leyland cylinder block included the
manifolds in a single casting and the overhead camshaft
was driven by eccentrics. Each cam operated an inlet and
exhaust valve by means of cantilever springs. The chassis
displayed such advanced features as torsion-bar springing
and vacuum assisted brakes. As the 7-litre engine
developed 145 h.p. the car had a phenomenal performance.
Such few Leylands as were built created a legend and were
a lasting tribute to the genius of Parry Thomas. But they
were a commercial failure and Leylands have never again
made a bid to enter the luxury car field. Towards the end
of the decade Vauxhall made an attempt to join the select
ranks of the luxury class with their 25/70 model. This car
was fitted with a six-cylinder single sleeve valve engine
designed by Burt, McCullum and Ricardo. This unit,
though very smooth and silent, was sluggish, a fact which,
taken in conjunction with inordinately heavy coachwork
made the car a disappointing performer considering that its
cost exceeded four figures. It is therefore not surprising

that it proved a costly failure. The Burt McCullum single sleeve valve principle has since been applied with more success to aero engines.

Finally, Bentleys tried to enter the luxury car market with their 8-litre model. Only a limited number of these fine though somewhat cumbersome cars were built before the firm got into difficulties and were taken over by Rolls Royce. It is difficult to resist the temptation to trace a connection between these two events and to believe that if the firm had concentrated on the production of its famous 3- and 4½-litre cars it might have maintained its separate existence.

As more and more cars appeared on the English roads, congested traffic conditions called for better brakes and led to the widespread introduction of front-wheel brakes in 1925. Certainly the capacity of the average car of 1923/4 to go greatly exceeded its capacity to stop. One manufacturer in his instruction book advised the driver to apply the handbrake " as soon as an obstacle is sighted," an adjuration which seemed to imply that the only hazards which the motorist was likely to encounter would be conveniently remote and static. In order to emphasise that they were liable to become static much more readily than their elder brethren, the new four-wheel braked cars proudly bore on their tails a red triangle sometimes accompanied by the legend " Caution Front-wheel Brakes."

On the smaller cars the first four-wheel brakes were direct operated, but on certain large and heavy cars foot power was assisted by a vacuum servo motor operating from the vacuum in the engine induction pipe. Before the end of the decade, however, the Lockheed hydraulic and the Bendix self-servo systems had appeared. This introduction of front-wheel brakes led to a general strengthening of chassis at the front end, and to the stiffening of front springs or shock absorbers in order to deal with the brake torque and the increased unsprung weight. They also brought about the speedy disappearance of transmission brakes.

The problems and dangers created by increasing traffic congestion resulted in other innovations, and many items hitherto regarded as " optional extras " became standard equipment. Safety glass for windscreens was introduced and finally was made compulsory by law. The problem of headlight dazzle arose and has been the subject of controversy ever since. Few cars built before 1927 had any means of controlling headlights other than an ' on and off " switch and one of the first efforts to deal with the problem was a mechanical system of dipping the headlamps by means of a hand lever such as that fitted to the Morris Oxford. This was soon surplanted by the solenoid " dip-and-switch " system in use today. Electric direction indicators or " trafficators " appeared as " extras " at the end of the '20s but soon became standard equipment, while warning brake " stop " lights were introduced at about the same time. Suction operated or electric windscreen wipers speedily replaced the crude manual type. The suction operated screen-wiper was never very satisfactory. Depending for its motive power on the vacuum created in the engine's induction pipe by the action of the throttle, it worked with totally unnecessary fury when the engine was idling, but when its efforts were really required with the throttle open and the car travelling at speed it frequently stopped altogether.

Wooden wheels, though they survived in America for a few more years, were not fitted in England after the war. In the '20s car wheels were of three types : the wire wheel of either stud fitting or " knock off " type, the ugly but strong steel " artillery " wheel and the solid disc. The excellence of the wire wheel has never been surpassed but it is difficult to clean and for this reason covering discs came into fashion. Disc wheels occasionally produce disconcerting results in a high cross wind, particularly when fitted to a very light car. On all types of wheel the old pattern " beaded edge " rim was superseded during the decade either by the " flat base " detachable rim type or by the modern pattern " well-base " rim. The wired edge tyres which fitted these new rims were of greater section, wider tread and carried a lower pressure. They were at first called " balloons " to distinguish them from the old high pressure type. This new method of attaching tyre to rim was much more positive, and the wheels of fast cars no longer displayed that formidable and (in the event of a puncture) maddening array of security bolts which were necessary to prevent beaded edge tyres from flying off.

Meanwhile the roads over which these tyres travelled were themselves being transformed by tarmacadam and bitumen, smooth and dustless but funereal, ugly and unsympathetic to everything other than wheeled traffic. Soon they were to be covered by thousands of miles of white lines, while already the danger signs were multiplying like weeds and the first robot traffic signals were blinking their red, green and amber eyes. These things were part of the price to be paid for the supremacy of internal combustion, but there was no one to ask whether the price might not prove to be too high. At road-side filling stations the first manual " Bowser " petrol pumps were becoming increasingly common. The petrol pump seems such an obvious improvement on the two-gallon can that one wonders why its coming was delayed so long. Perhaps safety regulations were responsible, although if this is the case they would appear to have been misguided. Recently, when I was looking through a copy of the R.A.C. *Journal* for 1914, I came across a photograph of soldiers filling petrol cans for use at the front. Petrol was being poured from a large barrel into what I can only describe as a kind of open horse-trough from beneath which hung a series of small pipes each of which was inserted into a can. Any device more fraught with the peril of sudden combustion it would be difficult to conceive.

If I were asked what, in my personal experience, I considered the most significant landmark in automobile history during the 1920's I would recall my visit to Shelsley Walsh hill-climb in the summer of 1926. At this meeting the prototype Riley 9 " Monaco " saloon made its bow to the Midlands public. I shall always remember the sensation caused when the car came up the hill and how we flocked to the finishing paddock at the top of the hill to make a closer examination. We had never seen anything like it before. How low it was ! Peering through the windows of the fabric body with its luggage boot at the rear we saw, not the expected flat floor and bench seats, but central gear change, sliding bucket seats in front and deep footwells set well below the line of the propeller shaft which was enclosed in a tunnel. It seemed to us hardly right that one should sit so near to the ground. The secret of this low centre of gravity lay not merely in the coachwork but in the dropped chassis frame which Victor Riley had evolved. Nor did the originality of the Riley stop short at the body and the frame. Though none of us realised it at the time there lurked under the bonnet an engine which was destined to form the basis of one of the most successful racing cars which England has yet evolved. For by the ingenious

PLATE 15

(*above*) *Luxury car : the* 1924 40/50 *h.p. Napier ;* (*below*) *Advanced design : the* 1929 *straight-eight Leyland Thomas.*

PLATE 16

*(above) A characteristic saloon car of the early '20's : the 15 h.p. Wolseley ; (below)
The shape of things to come : the 9 h.p. Riley " Monaco " saloon of 1926.*

use of twin camshafts mounted high in the crankcase and operating inclined valves through short push-rods, Riley obtained by the simplest means a perfect hemispherical combustion chamber, well cooled and with a large port area. The Riley 9 was not designed as a sports car ; on the contrary the efficiency of the engine was utilised to propel a car which far exceeded in roominess any other make of the same nominal horse-power. Nevertheless the potentialities of the Riley engine were quickly realised and turned to good account.

The Riley Monaco Saloon had a very great influence upon the design of the small and medium-powered car for the next decade. It also accelerated the changeover from open to closed cars. This is probably the most striking phenomenon in the history of the motor trade and one for which it is very difficult to account. In 1925 open cars were still in the majority on English roads, but so swift was the reversal of public demand that within ten years their numbers had shrunk to a very small minority. It may be argued that the saloon car is the obvious answer to the vagaries of the English climate, but this does not explain why the open car was still the popular choice in 1925 when nearly all manufacturers offered alternative closed coachwork. Perhaps the explanation may lie in the fact that in 1925 motoring was still for the majority a pleasurable indulgence whereas a decade later the average car had become, to a far greater extent, a utilitarian all-weather method of transport.

The average four-seater open car of 1925 was not very different in appearance from the " torpedo " tourer of 1914. A high two-piece windscreen, the top half opening outwards, and numerous detachable celluloid side-screens provided weather protection which was augmented, in many cases, by a second windscreen with dependent apron for the benefit of the rear passengers. In fine weather the hood was usually furled at the rear in a hood cover, but occasionally, as on the Ruston-Hornsby, it was of the " disappearing " type which folded into a well behind the rear seat back. Incidentally these hoods substantially exceeded the width of the body, the tops of the side curtains being attached to interior valances. This effectually prevented rainwater from running off the hood and into the car. Such a provision may appear elementary, yet it has been overlooked on many modern open cars.

Right-hand gate change and handbrake, a flat floor and what is now called a " bench " seat enabled many " two-seaters " to seat three in front in reasonable comfort, but the unfortunate occupant of the dickey seat behind was generally very far from comfortable. Not only was he left fully exposed to the elements, but the dickey seat itself often left much to be desired. On the earlier post-war cars the boot lid folded back into a horizontal position to reveal a thinly upholstered seat pad on it underside and a folding back rest. This form of dickey seat might have been designed, like the old church pews, with the deliberate intention of circumventing any attempt at relaxation. It also left the occupant perched on the car rather than in it. Mercifully, this ingenious form of torture was soon superceded by a dickey of more familiar type in which the curved boot-lid formed a back-rest when opened and the passenger sat within the body. This change also considerably improved the appearance of the rear of the car.

A few ingenious and presentable two and four-seater drop-head bodies were available by the middle '20s, though the average low-priced saloon car was high, square and ugly. But at the same period specialist coachbuilders were building on luxury chassis magnificent closed coachwork of dateless excellence. In my opinion the most elegant body ever designed was the Coupé de Ville which was to be seen on certain cars, notably Rolls Royce and Delage, before the end of the '20s. Basketwork covered the lower panels of the black, knife-edged coupé which mounted, by a delightful convention, a pair of square candle-type side lamps. Our demagogues might comment adversely upon the contrast between the accommodation for driver and passenger in the Coupé de Ville, but it did not belong to this age. It was the craftsman coachbuilder's last backward glance at an age of different values which had passed away.

From 1926 onwards closed cars, following the pattern set by the Riley Monaco, multiplied rapidly and the right-hand gate change, bench seat and flat floor became practically extinct. The advantages of the bucket seat were that it was adjustable and that it prevented the occupant from sliding about on corners. But it banished any possibility of seating three in front and proved to be more tiring on a long journey because it allowed little or no change of position. That these faults are evidently recognized is apparent from the return of the wide bench seat now that dashboard or steering column gear control has once more permitted a clear floor.

Another Riley feature which was generally adopted was the built-in rear luggage boot, and into this the spare wheel, always a headache to the symmetrically minded designer, presently disappeared for good. Hitherto it had occasionally been mounted externally at the rear, but more commonly on the off-side running board. Its disappearance has certainly improved the looks of the motor-car, but its hiding place is sometimes inaccessible, particularly when luggage is carried. Moreover it is apt to be accidentally or intentionally forgotten when tyre pressures are checked with the result that when it is required (perhaps on a dark winter's night) it is found to be flat.

The adoption by Rileys of the fabric body on a wooden frame was also widely followed, though this vogue was short-lived. The genuine Weymann fabric body was a sound and durable job, and many of them can still be seen on the road in excellent condition at the present time. But unfortunately several car manufacturers produced their own fabric bodies using shoddy and rickety frames and inferior fabric. In a short time the frames rattled themselves to pieces, the fabric crazed, cracked and split and the resulting tattered spectacles of rapid dissolution brought all fabric bodies into unmerited disfavour. Moreover the age of pressed steel bodywork was at hand, and this banished both fabric and coach panelled bodies from all but the most costly cars.

In America, Henry Ford had developed the system of mass-production by intensive mechanisation and standardisation as early as 1910 when he launched the famous " Model T " upon the world. By 1915, when an average 12 h.p. English car cost between £350 and £400, a fully equipped 20 h.p. Ford two-seater was listed in England at £115. For a time the war and the post-war demand for cars at any price obscured the significance of this fact. It is true that in the early '20s quantity production methods were introduced by Clyno and Morris but they did not attempt to emulate the far more intensive methods used by Ford. Henry Ford made no secret of his methods, in fact he invited English manufacturers to inspect his plant at Trafford Park. The English car manufacturer had built up a tradition of individual character and quality which he was reluctant to abandon for the soulless mechanical precision of the Ford technique. But when the post-war boom was over and economic depression set in, it became increasingly apparent that, if it was to survive, the English motor industry must reorganise itself on the American model. Thus it came about that the end of the '20s witnessed the dawn of the age of mass production in England and a great formative era of fine engineering craftsmanship drew to a close.

CHAPTER SIX

THE AGE OF MASS PRODUCTION
AND MONOPOLY

THE APPLICATION of the principles of mass production to the English motor industry brought about a profound change, not merely to manufacturing methods but to the whole constitution of the industry and to the cars which it produced. Hitherto, although manufacturers had evolved certain techniques peculiar to the industry, the motor-car was the product of a combination of human skill and machine tools very similar to that employed to construct a railway locomotive or any other similar product of English mechanical engineering genius. Components received from foundry, forge or rolling mill were machined by power tools of comparatively simple form and function which, in the course of their long evolution throughout the nineteenth century had become as commonplace and familiar to the mechanical engineer as the saw, chisel and plane in the country carpenter's rush basket. The fashioning of these components by means of these tools and their successful marriage in the complete car called for a high degree of skill in machine, fitting and erecting shops the quality of which was reflected in the finished product. Under such a system, the number of cars produced was relatively low in proportion to the number of workmen employed. But the comparatively little capital required to build cars by these methods enabled a large number of small firms to enter the trade. The customer benefited both from the keen competition between these firms and from the very wide range of cars available. Moreover, because production methods relying primarily on human skill are essentially versatile, individual manufacturers were readily able either to produce a variety of models or so to vary one particular model that it virtually became a " bespoke " car, modified to meet the customer's individual requirements. In this way the needs and individual tastes of the motorist were very fairly met, while conversely he was often able to exercise a positive influence on development. Because the manufacturing capital involved was relatively small, by far the greater proportion of the purchase price of a motor car was represented by the cost of the materials and the skill which had gone into its construction. Thus, in intrinsic terms, the motorist got very good value for his money even though the car might not be " cheap " in the modern sense of the word.

The technique of manufacture evolved by Henry Ford completely changed all this, and its principle can best be explained by one simple illustration. Whereas, let us say, the English manufacturer had been accustomed to drill the thirty holes in the sump flange of a crank-case casting with the aid of a single spindle drilling machine, the Ford technique would introduce a specially designed machine with multiple heads which could not only drill the thirty holes in the sump flange at once, but simultaneously perform a similar operation on the vertical timing case and clutch-housing faces. With such a machine, machining time, and consequently labour cost, might be reduced fifty times. In this way, Ford argued, the price of the finished car could be enormously reduced while it would nevertheless be possible for the machine operator to earn much higher wages on account of his increased " productivity." There are very serious flaws in this argument, but since it is still current today it is scarcely surprising that the English Motor Industry should have accepted it with alacrity as a way out of their difficulties in the slump period of 1929–31.

Present-day mechanical and scientific ingenuity is such that, from the strictly technical point of view, it is hard to envisage any limit to the extent to which the principle of mass production can be developed unless it be the entirely automatic procreation of machines by machines. Once accepted, in fact, mass production methods must develop towards this ultimate end although, by doing so, they involve either the supercession of men by machines, or a continual expansion of production. With the social and political stresses and strains occasioned by such inevitable expansion we are already painfully familiar although we seldom recognise their cause. Still less do we recognise, unfortunately, the fact that mass production cannot increase by one jot the earth's basic resources of food and raw materials upon which the continued survival of the human race depends. The ingenuity, complexity and boundless facility of modern mass production methods so dazzle us that we become blind to the simple fact that they are methods of conversion and not of creation. The manufacturer cannot, for example, create the mineral ores and other raw materials which go to make a motor-car any more than he could create the mineral oil which, in the form of petrol, goes into its tank. All that mass production has achieved in this respect is to enable man to expend these exhaustible resources on an unprecedented scale.

These might be called the general and long-term flaws in Henry Ford's " productivity " argument. There are other and more immediate effects which dim the bright lustre of the mass production theory and which are well illustrated by the recent history of the motor industry. It will be obvious that elaborate machines such as the multi-spindle driller, which has been cited as an example, are infinitely more costly than the simpler tools which they replaced. Hence the fact that a very considerable proportion of the price of a mass-produced motor-car represents the capital cost, maintenance and depreciation of the plant required to make it and not the labour and materials expended upon it. This proportion increases the more mass production methods are applied, and the effect is that though the car so produced may become progressively " cheaper," its intrinsic value to the purchaser becomes lower. To explain this by practical example, it has been calculated that a small mass-produced car of the middle '30s selling at £125 cost the manufacturer from £12 to £15 in labour and materials, the balance being accounted for by plant and administrative overheads, advertising costs and the profits claimed by manufacturers, distributors and agents. Although I have no figures to support the contention, I would guess that a light car of similar size built by a small manufacturer in the early '20s would cost approximately double its successor, but that out of this £250 at least 50 per cent would be required to cover labour and materials. This rapid decline in quality and intrinsic value profoundly changed the attitude of the average motorist towards his car. In the early '20s he valued his car not only for what it would *do* but for what it *was*, but along with American methods of mass production came the American view which regarded the car merely as a convenient means of transport to be discarded as lightly as a worn pair of shoes when its brief working life was done.

For an industry organised on mass production lines it is

very important that the customer should regard the product in this way. Firstly, expansive " flow production " largely relies on a rapid replacement rate to keep its wheels turning ; secondly, it was essential for technical reasons that the customer should not be selective and critical. For an efficient mass production plant cannot admit individual variations or a multiplicity of models and must discourage radical changes of design except at very infrequent intervals because, unlike the older manufacturing principle, it is not versatile. The use of complex and costly machines of highly specialised function which may demand days of highly skilled work to tool and set up for a given operation is only economic for " long runs " of the same component. The maximum degree of standardisation therefore becomes the aim, the ideal, as Henry Ford demonstrated, being " one model " production over a long period. Furthermore, when a new model is to be introduced a compromise takes place and the design of the car is adapted to the requirements and limitations of the plant in preference to the more costly course of adapting the plant to the best design. Thus quality is sacrificed to the expediency of quantity and " cheapness," while the ultimate arbiter of the mass-produced car ceases to be the motorist or even the designer but the machine as personified by the production engineer and his fellow technicians. Hence the fact that the conversion of the English motor industry to mass production was accompanied by a great increase in advertising and high-pressure salesmanship all of which was devoted to persuading the more gullible motorists that the standards which the new manufacturing methods so arbitrarily prescribed were in fact just those qualities which he had always wanted and for which he had hitherto waited in vain.

This task was simplified by the rapid trend of the industry from great diversity towards a monopoly which considerably restricted the motorist's range of choice. Where before a number of small firms had keenly competed for his patronage, now a few large manufacturing groups offered him their new models with a show of bland complacency which implied that he was blessed indeed to be able to buy them. The tendency towards monopoly was partly a result of the financial crisis and partly the inevitable accompaniment of the changeover to mass production methods. Only one or two of the largest motor manufacturing organisations could command the necessary capital resources to re-equip their factories on the American model. Some of the smaller concerns vanished altogether; some ceased building cars and turned to other engineering activities better suited to small scale production; some either sold out to large English or American organisations or combined with other small firms; a few, happily, have been able to survive and so maintain a qualitative tradition.

The organisation of the large firms which emerged from this period of transition took two forms. Companies which had proved powerful enough to retain their individual identity in fact as well as in name tended to concentrate all their activities in one huge plant. "Combines" of hitherto independent firms, on the other hand, allocated specialised functions to the hitherto self-sufficient factories of their several members. Thus one plant would become responsible for engines, another for axles, gearboxes and other components, and another for assembly. The sales value of the prestige which the cars of constituent companies had rightly earned during an independent career which often dated from the birth of the industry was recognised, and for this reason their products continued, nominally, to retain their individual identity. I use the word nominally because this policy, more often than not, did little more than deceive the ignorant or pander to the snob. It certainly produced results which distressed the enthusiast and the student of automobile history alike. The proud radiator and bonnet characteristic of some famous marque would be found to conceal a mediocre side-valve engine distinguished only from that fitted to another and equally mediocre car by a sprinkling of plated parts. Or a typical mass-produced Anglo-American saloon would appear, boasting of its great tradition and bearing a caricature of the insignia of one of the most famous and historic sports cars ever built.

The appearance of the mass produced car was generally inferior to that of its predecessor. Hitherto, every part of the car had a definite function to perform, and the appearance of the complete car depended upon the proportion and perfection of these parts both individually and in relation to each other. In fact, like all machines, the beauty of the motor-car is essentially functional as a consideration of a " Silver Ghost " Rolls Royce or a Grand Prix racing car will reveal. Now it might have been supposed that the mass produced car would be functional in the most elementary sense, but this was not the case ; instead, for the first time, the car began to grow " frills " whose sole function was to disguise or conceal inferior workmanship or, like the thin sugar coating on a bitter pill, to impart a meretricious show-room glitter. The imposing radiator became a false façade of thin sheet metal with a dummy cap. The real radiator, efficient but cheap and crudely finished, lurked under the bonnet, its filler cap so situated that it could only be topped up with the utmost inconvenience and its drain tap diabolically inaccessible. Like Adam when he had eaten of the Tree of Knowledge, the motor-car no longer went naked and unashamed but proceeded to clothe itself in garments of sheet metal. Unlike Adam, however, it was with good reason that the more intimate parts of its anatomy were thus hidden from the public gaze. Dire disorders could beset these coyly concealed components without the unfortunate owner being aware of the fact, while before he could effect a remedy the equally unfortunate mechanic must needs wrestle with the rusted screws which buttoned up their tinny clothing.

Because, in a machine, appearance is a derivative of function, many other changes which were made in the mass produced car adversely affected both. The manufacturers of the past had found that with orthodox suspension the best road-holding and cornering qualities were secured by concentrating the weight as much as possible towards the centre of the chassis. The engine was therefore mounted well back so that the position of the radiator was either behind or directly above the centre-line of the front axle. Now, on the pretext of securing a greater body space than the chassis could properly accommodate, the engine was moved forward over the axle. This gave the car an ungainly front-heavy appearance. In fact it *was* front heavy. This vice, combined with hydraulic shock absorbers which would have been incapable of damping a car of half the weight, large low pressure tyres and light, low geared and inaccurate steering produced bad and even positively dangerous handling qualities. The argument that racing car standards of roadworthiness are unnecessary in a small " family car " is as specious as it is dangerous, for in the life of every car there may come an emergency—an error of judgment, an icy road—when such standards become a matter of life or death. However competent he might be, the driver of the average small saloon car of the middle

'30s could do little more than trust in providence when faced with a sudden emergency.

Another contribution to the deterioration of roadworthiness was the introduction of flexible rubber engine mountings which robbed the front end of the chassis frame of its most valuable cross-bracing. This form of mounting, which obviated the need for careful dynamic engine balancing, was hailed by the sales departments as a wonderful invention for overcoming engine vibration. In fact, the ill-balanced engine often grew so restless in its rubber bed that the radiator hose connections split, the long whippy gear lever lashed to and fro in the driving compartment, and the whole car trembled with an animation that no rubber mountings could quell. Moreover, if one of the hose connections split the unfortunate driver might be stranded for the rest of the day. For instead of connecting engine and radiator with short straight lengths of hose between cast or drawn metal pipes, mass production had found it cheaper to produce special moulded rubber connections of varying diameter and serpentine form.

This catalogue of decadence could be prolonged indefinitely. Positive controls by rods and links were replaced by Heath Robinson devices of piano wire and springs. In place of plated brass, steel or aluminium for small castings and fittings, extensive use was made of an extremely brittle form of zinc alloy die casting which broke as readily as glass to leave a dangerous ragged edge. Some manufacturers even used this material for steering-wheels, a criminal economy which, in the event of accident, must have accounted for many broken ribs and punctured lungs. The solid wooden dashboard set with a row of individual, easily read instruments was replaced by a metal or plastic fascia finished to simulate wood in which was mounted a single multiple instrument incorporating a number of small illegible dials whose needles pointed confusingly in different directions. Instead of a fold-flat or two-piece windscreen, manufacturers either fixed the single-piece windscreen irrevocably or permitted it to open enough to produce a howling draught about the region of the second waist-coat button, but not enough to clear the line of vision. This greatly increased the difficulty of driving in thick fog or frost. Ground clearance was often reduced to an extent that made the passage of badly rutted or flooded roads impossible, while the major components became so inaccessible that the simplest owner-maintenance was impossible without the aid of a pit or some form of car lift. Punctures acquired a new terror because in order to get the jack into position under the axle the unfortunate driver must needs prostrate himself in the road, a proceeding scarcely calculated to improve the temper, particularly on a wet winter's night. Some manufacturers, however, displayed the quality of mercy by installing hydraulic or manual permanent jacks or a type of portable jack which could be attached to bumpers or running boards. Wheel changing would have been still further simplified if more manufacturers had adopted the Rudge type wheel and hub with " knock off " cap, but so far from becoming more common this admirable device has grown steadily rarer in recent years so that the driver seems doomed forever to fumble and grope with a ring of small wheel nuts.

Most cars of the '30s carried beneath their bonnets what can only be called a vestigial starting handle. When the electric starter became universal it was natural that the old fixed starting handle should become detachable, but mechanical vagaries are such that the handle is still an essential item of equipment. To provide for this purpose a long,

crude and whippy piece of bent iron and to omit from the
chassis any adequate steady bearing for the same was quite
inexcusable. Woe betide the wretched motorist condemned
by frosty weather or a flat battery to start his engine with
such an implement !

One of the most melancholy symptoms of decline was
the marked deterioration in engine durability. There were
several reasons for this. In the first place, in their efforts to
obtain better top gear flexibility from the inherently in-
flexible small bore and long stroke engines which the
method of horse-power taxation had brought into being,
manufacturers fitted progressively lower top gear ratios.
Piston speed thus became inordinately high in relation to
road speed so that the little engines literally racked themselves to an early death. Bad design and poor quality materials hastened their end. Too low a working temperature
and bad distribution of the cooling water entering the
cylinder block increased the rate of cylinder wear by pro-
longing the critical warming-up period when, as a result of
corrosive action, cylinder walls are most vulnerable. The
detachable cylinder blocks of the older cars were cast in an
iron of exceptionally fine grain, the castings being often
allowed to weather in the rough for months before they
were machined. This quality, combined with a properly
designed cooling system resulted in a car which would run
for years without a re-bore. That this is no exaggeration
may be instanced by the fact that my own 1926 12/50
Alvis, still in regular use at the time of writing, has been
fitted with one new set of piston rings but has never yet
been re-bored and consumes a negligible quantity of oil.
With the spread of mass production methods the combination of cylinder block and crankcase in one casting became
practically universal and it was no longer considered econo-

PLATE 17

Ageless Craftsmanship : 1925 Phantom I Rolls Royce with Coupé de Ville body.

PLATE 18

THE AGE OF MASS PRODUCTION: CAUSE AND EFFECT

(above) The 1923 " Model T " Ford saloon ; (below) Traffic congestion on Watling Street near Rochester, 1939.

mic to use the same high quality material for this larger casting. A soft coarse grained material was not only cheaper but could be machined more readily. For these reasons the average small car of the 1930s rarely exceeded 40,000 miles without a re-bore except at the cost of excessive oil consumption.

Mass production was by no means confined to the chassis of the car, but extended to the body and to the auxiliaries. Rapid developments in the technique of sheet metal press-work and fabrication by electric arc welding made possible the quantity production of all steel bodies. This soon confined the centuries old tradition of the craftsman coach-builder and upholsterer to a handful of specialist coach-builders whose reputation had been built in the days before the internal combustion engine. The all-steel body was undoubtedly superior to the ill-made coachbuilt bodies which appeared on some of the cheaper English cars of the period immediately prior to mass production. Unlike the latter, the steel body did not rattle and disintegrate and its construction was very much stronger and consequently safer in the event of accident. In view of the inherent instability of many of the chassis to which it was fitted, this last was a very decisive advantage. But the steel body acted as a convenient sounding board for mechanical noises. It was also cold in winter and hot in summer, while the method of trimming with rexine-covered sheets of plywood or cardboard held in place by self-tapping screws would have made any self-respecting coach trimmer turn in his grave.

The introduction of the all-steel body coincided with the appearance of cellulose finish. Cellulose spraying produces a better, cheaper and more durable result than an indifferent coach finish. But compared with the richness, depth and lustre of the highest quality coach painting, cellulose has what can only be described as a " cheap look " such as differentiates a japanned biscuit tin from a piece of Battersea or Bilston enamel. Cellulose is subject to rapid oxidisation which produces a dull bloom and to maintain a high polish this bloom must be continually removed until eventually the bare metal appears.

Another change which took place at this time was the supercession of nickel by chromium plate for radiators, lamps and other plated parts. Nickel plate, like the earlier brass or copper, tarnished rapidly if not polished but its gleaming surface not only reflected but amply rewarded the labour spent upon it. Chromium plate, on the other hand, requires little or no labour because it is virtually untarnishable, but its cold, blue meretricious glitter holds little pleasure for the eye. Those who consider that this is merely conservative and prejudiced opinion should compare the best specimen of chromium plating available with the polished surface of a nickel-silver radiator as fitted to Vauxhalls during the early '20s.

For many years the production of electrical and other auxiliary equipment had not been undertaken by car manufacturers but by a number of specialist firms who offered manufacturers a wide range of type and quality. In this field the application of mass production methods had a precisely similar result as in the parent industry. Rapid progress towards monopoly was accompanied by an equally rapid deterioration in the quality of equipment. This set a problem to the few surviving manufacturers who were concerned to maintain the quality of their cars, and at least one of them found the solution by installing equipment made by a famous Continental firm.

It is time to turn from this sad chronicle of decline and

fall and to consider instead the chief developments of the period from 1930 until the outbreak of the second world war. Of these the most important was the disappearance of the old " crash " gearbox which had persisted, basically unchanged, since the days of the first Panhard et Levassor. Of all the controls of the motor-car the novice regarded the gear lever with by far the greatest trepidation. Often he was never able to master that automatic co-ordination of foot and hand on clutch, accelerator and lever which ensured a smooth and silent change of speed. Consequently the roads of the '20s frequently resounded with a sound like that made by a circular saw as it strikes a nail in a plank. Mechanically minded listeners visibly winced as some driver endeavoured forcibly to engage together two gear wheels revolving at widely different velocities. Designers therefore devoted considerable attention to the evolution of simpler methods of changing speed. The first and most obvious simplification had been to keep the gears constantly in mesh and to effect changes of speed by means of sliding dog clutches. This was further developed by substituting for a simple dog a device consisting of tapering steel rollers or cones which enabled any difference in speed between driving and driven members to be taken up smoothly. At first, most manufacturers confined the application of " synchro-mesh," as it was called, to third speed only, but others, of whom the Alvis Company were among the first, produced gearboxes fitted with synchro-mesh engagement of all four speeds.

A more revolutionary development was the " self-change " gearbox, as evolved by Wilson and E.N.V., which embodied in a much refined form the epicyclic gears originally used by F. W. Lanchester and later applied by Henry Ford to his " Model T." The epicyclic principle

consists of the employment of a " sun and planet " gear
which either transmits power directly when the whole unit
is free to revolve, or at a reduced ratio through the gears
when the outer member is held stationary by means of a
contracting brake band. Whereas the " Model T " used
only two units to provide two forward speeds (direct and
indirect) and reverse, the Wilson and E.N.V. boxes offered
the full complement of four speeds and reverse. Moreover an ingenious operating mechanism enabled the next
speed required to be " pre-selected " by a small lever on the
steering column whereupon the action of a foot pedal
released and applied the appropriate brake-bands. The
self-change gearbox did not obviate the use of some form
of clutch between engine and gearbox. In some cars,
notably the Talbot, the change-speed pedal also released a
clutch of normal type when depressed, but this dual function sometimes (on the " Firefly " Alvis for example) called
for excessive pedal pressure. Daimler and Lanchester
solved the problem by means of a hydraulic drive unit consisting of vaned rotors running in oil which became known
as a " fluid flywheel," while other manufacturers such as
Rileys used a centrifugal clutch. Both these units engaged
automatically when the engine was speeded up and released
when it slowed to idling speed. Both possessed the disadvantage that they could not transmit power " in reverse "
—that is to say from the road wheels to the engine. This
meant that the engines of cars so fitted could not be started
by pushing, coasting or towing, expedients which sometimes become necessary even with the best of cars as a result
of battery failure, extreme cold, damp, or tight bearings.

The self-change gearbox operated very successfully, but
compared with the orthodox " straight " gearbox it was
large and complex in proportion to the power transmitted

and possessed a lower mechanical efficiency. When employed in a car of really high power and performance the brake bands needed frequent renewal.

More ambitious experiments of the period were the Constantinesco and the Hayes gearboxes which were no less than attempts to achieve that ideal which has haunted designers like the alchemist's dream of transmutation—the automatic, infinitely variable speed gear. At one time the Hayes gearbox was actually fitted on an optional basis to certain Austin cars. Its operating principle was developed from that of the synchro-mesh cones, the cones themselves being in this case wholly responsible for transmitting the drive.

The last addition to the ranks of easy change gearboxes was the Cotal, originally evolved on the Continent. In this device both selection and engagement are effected by electrical means. Though complex it is at once less cumbersome and more efficient than its predecessors and is becoming increasingly popular at the present time.

Increasingly congested traffic conditions led designers to pay more attention to brakes, and although some car manufacturers continued to design their own braking systems, some, such as the Rover, being highly efficient, the majority adopted one of the three proprietary types which dominated the field : Bendix self-servo, Lockheed hydraulic, or the Girling type which employed a wedge instead of the traditional cam to expand the shoes. On some mass-produced cars grossly undersized drums were fitted so that a high pressure had to be applied to the limited braking surface available. This involved very frequent adjustment and relining, while excessive heat was generated on heavy braking which caused the thin drums to expand. This defect was not assisted by the fact that little or no attention.

was paid to drum cooling by induced ventilation or finning. Again, many braking systems were not progressive in application, that is to say braking power was not proportionate to pedal pressure, a defect which was apt to produce surprising results on a greasy or icy surface. Nevertheless though their braking behaviour might leave much to be desired, there can be little doubt that in sheer stopping power the average car of the 1930s compared favourably with the majority of its predecessors.

A positive improvement in the car's electrical equipment which was widely introduced in this period was the voltage control system which automatically regulated the output of the dynamo in accordance with the needs of the battery. This arrangement, by preventing over-charging, undoubtedly prolonged the life of the storage battery. Such a safeguard had become essential in view of the greatly increased burden which the car battery was now called upon to bear. Quite apart from its essential functions it must needs supply a plethora of auxiliaries : trafficators ; twin horns ; fog or pass lights ; brake and reversing lights ; windscreen wipers and de-frosters ; interior lights ; a cigarette lighter ; an electric clock and perhaps a car radio set. Concerning the last-mentioned gadget my personal prejudice is so strong that discretion warns me not to air it here.

The most striking change in the electrical department at this time was the swift and almost universal change from magneto back to coil ignition. Thus, after reigning supreme for nearly thirty years, the magneto was deposed by a development of the system which it had superseded. Magneto and coil have opposite characteristics, the efficiency of the former increasing with engine speed and vice versa. Therefore the coil system produces the best low speed spark which assists starting, but is less suitable for ultra high-speed engines, while it has the added disadvantage of making the car wholly dependent on its battery. A magneto of really good quality is a reliable but very costly instrument whereas a reliable coil system can be produced more cheaply and is simpler. On balance, therefore, the change was justified, although the best of both worlds was secured by those few manufacturers who, like Rolls Royce, fitted both systems.

The use of new types of carburettor operating on the " down-draught " principle improved volumetric efficiency, while the high octane fuels which the new electric pumps delivered enabled compression ratios to be raised. As a result, even the most mediocre-looking side-valve engine unit produced, during its brief life, an astonishing power output for its size, though often with considerable fuss and less fuel economy than its predecessors.

The gravity petrol tank under the scuttle, the Autovac operating by engine suction and the old air pressure system all disappeared in favour of electric pumps or mechanical diaphragm pumps, driven from the engine camshaft, which fed the carburettor from the rear tank.

New or improved components evolved by specialist manufacturers brought about proportionate improvements in the complete car provided they were properly and adequately applied. Among them may be mentioned smaller sparking plugs which made possible more generous cylinder head cooling ; " thin shell " crankshaft bearings in place of the heavy white-metal type ; " Silentbloc " and oil-less bushes which required no lubrication and prevented rattles, and needle-roller bearings which reduced the weight and increased the life of propeller shafts.

Towards the end of the period, independent wheel suspension began to make its appearance on popular cars, but since its evolution was soon interrupted by the war its consideration may appropriately be postponed to another chapter.

To sum up the situation as it stood on the eve of the second world war it must be said that in spite of all these technical innovations the average English car of 1939 compared unfavourably with the car of the middle '20s. Increased technical knowledge was more than offset by a poverty of execution inherent in the mass production principle. The dictatorship of the machine and the assembly line with its emphasis on quantity rather than quality and the monopoly in the manufacture of components together effectually hamstrung the designer and the craftsman whose combined skill had hitherto built motor-cars worthy of the great tradition of English mechanical engineering.

So much for the effect of mass production methods on the motor-car itself. When the English manufacturers were busy re-planning their factories on the American model no one seems to have paused to consider what would happen when the little tin cars of the new age began to pour from the assembly tracks on to the roads of England like peas out of bursting pods. Yet if the powers that preside at Euston had without premeditation suddenly decided to divert all the traffic from their Crewe main line to some single track branch the result would not have been dissimilar. In fact the parallel would be more exact if we imagine that at the same time, as a result of a strike, all the train crews were replaced by amateurs and all the signalmen left their posts. City streets became jammed with traffic to the point of chaos ; narrow main roads constantly presented scenes of disaster phenomenally avoided as the " man in the street " light-heartedly indulged for the first time in the joys of a road no longer " open " in a car whose speed exceeded both its safety factor and its driver's skill. With each successive holiday season traffic on the roads from city to coast slowed from a death-defying scramble to a procession and from a procession to a crawling continuous queue of cars which justified the slogan " It's Quicker by Rail." No wonder the toll of road accident casualties soared ; no wonder motorists, good and bad alike, found themselves cabined and confined by successive restrictions both legal and physical, expediencies forced upon authority in its desperate efforts to bring order out of chaos. Compulsory insurance and driving tests were introduced, while the roads themselves grew to resemble those children's parlour games where counters move obedient to the throw of dice around a board beset by penalties and hazards. Confronted by innumerable robot traffic signals, by roundabouts, by pedestrian crossings, by one-way streets, by parking prohibitions and by speed restriction signs an older generation of motorists sighed for the spacious days of the early '20s which had gone forever. With the object of relieving congestion and reducing accidents, towns were by-passed by new roads, dangerous corners were widened and eased and cross roads staggered. Though these developments certainly improved traffic flow, they did little or nothing to reduce the toll of casualties, while they certainly made no contribution to the English scene. They enabled the inexperienced to travel even faster, a circumstance made doubly dangerous by the fact that no attempt was made to prevent the new by-pass roads becoming built-up areas. Highways such as the Great West Road out of London became far more fraught with peril than the older routes which they relieved.

With the roadside suburban houses which the new mobility made possible came all-electric "super-service" stations, advertising signs innumerable, ramshackle transport cafés, olde worlde tea barns, bathing lidos, and monstrous new pubs or roadhouses which were grotesque caricatures or admixtures of every conceivable architectural style. Mile upon mile of main road became an urban corridor linking one town with the next and insulating the traveller from a countryside in full retreat. It was as though the age of mass production had, almost overnight, conjured up a new civilisation; a gimcrack press-button civilisation of chromium plate, neon sign, juke box and pin table which had about it that unsubstantial, nightmare unreality of the film set where things are never what they seem. This strange synthetic world seemed to beget a restless and rootless population of its own with its own peculiar underworld. The shady dealer in second-hand cars who asked no questions, the car bandit and the lorry-hopping harlot, these were the successors of the horse dealers, the highwaymen and the tavern strumpets of a bygone age.

To what end this world would have developed had not the second world war intervened it is idle to speculate. Perhaps it is true to say that it could have come to no other end.

CHAPTER SEVEN

THE RACING CAR

BECAUSE IT HAS been legally debarred from our public roads, and because English manufacturers have never appreciated its technical and advertising value to the same extent as their Continental rivals, this country has only made a minor contribution to motor-racing history. Nevertheless, racing has undoubtedly played a very important part in the evolution of the English car. The industry probably does not appreciate the debt which it owes to those few firms who, in the past, had the enterprise and courage to build special racing cars and with them challenge the Continental masters on their own ground. In this way they not only evolved important innovations themselves as a result of the lessons learnt in the hard school of long-distance road racing; they also became familiar with the latest Continental developments as they were embodied in the cars against which they competed, and in this way English design was kept abreast of the times.

We find improved features of design first manifested in a Grand Prix racing car, then appearing on a high-grade production sports car, and finally becoming a commonplace of standard car design. Thus it comes about that a new and successful racing car design is generally the portent of future standard practice. The fact that the racing car's original features often become unhappily caricatured by the time they reach the cheap car production line is another matter the reason for which has already been discussed.

In terms of speed as we know it, the very first Continental road events were tests of reliability rather than races. Levassor's winning speed on his 4 h.p. Panhard in the Paris-Bordeaux Race of 1895 was only 15 m.p.h. Yet this achievement was in reality a tremendous feat of sheer physical effort and endurance. The modern motorist who feels fatigued after coaxing his temperamental veteran over 56 miles of smooth tarmac from London to Brighton should reflect that to achieve his victory Levassor nursed his crude vehicle with its tiller steering over 732 miles of rough roads, driving continuously for two days and forty-eight minutes.

Levassor's car of 1895 was virtually a standard model—if any car could be called standard at that time—but from 1897 onwards specialised racing cars began to develop. At first, however, this was a specialisation not so much of brains as of brute force since it was directed, not towards improving the efficiency of a given engine but to reconciling the lightest possible vehicle with the largest possible engine. Perhaps the most valuable result of this line of development was that it encouraged the use of light alloys and stronger materials, weight for weight. How rapid it was may be judged by the fact that the Mors racing car of 1901 had a 10-litre engine of 60 h.p. In the same year Napier constructed an even larger car with a capacity of 13 litres which covered 5 miles at an average of 67 m.p.h. But the big Napier made havoc of the pneumatic tyres of the period and was useless for long distance racing on this account. Tyres were, in fact, the only factor controlling growth until the Automobile Club de France, the great patrons and organisers of the sport at this time, became alarmed and imposed a formula limiting the weight of cars to 1,000 kilos or approximately 1 ton. Unfortunately for the A.C.F. this formula did not have the desired effect. Designers succeeded in producing even larger engines while still contriving to keep within the weight limit. The 90 h.p. Panhard of 1905 with its 15-litre engine was the ultimate achievement in this direction although by then it had already become an archaic type. Where the 1,000 kilo formula did not apply, even more monstrous vehicles appeared, the palm for sheer size going to the Fiat of 1911 which had an enormous four-cylinder engine of 300 h.p. and 28½ litres capacity, the bore and stroke being 190 × 230 mm.

Truly it may be said that there were giants in those days, and the names of Panhard, Mors, Gobron-Brillie, Richard Brasier, Mercedes, Fiat, de Dietrich, Renault and Itala have become legendary. So too, have the names of the men who drove these thunderous monsters, not within the circumscribed bounds of a track, but from Paris to Berlin, Vienna or Bordeaux on rough roads, through choking clouds of dust and over tortuous mountain passes. And this with cars having flimsy wooden chassis strengthened with flitch plates, narrow tyres liable to fail at any time, weak suspension and ineffective brakes. It was under conditions such as this that Renee de Knyff, Fournier, Farman, Gabriel, Thery, Marcelle Renault and Camille Jenatzy won their place in motoring history. Not least among them was our own Charles Jarrott. No matter what dire misfortunes befell him, Jarrott's motto was " Always finish," and in his book *Ten Years of Motors and Motor Racing* there is a wonderful account of the Paris-Vienna race of 1902 in which Jarrott describes how he and his mechanic du Cros dismembered the furniture in their hotel bedroom at Bregenz to manufacture a splint for the broken frame of their Panhard.

Besides Jarrott and S. F. Edge, whose victory in the Gordon-Bennett Race of 1902 with a Napier has already been mentioned, Clifford Earp, Stead and Lorraine Barrow were other Englishmen who raced against the Continental drivers. Jarrott, Stead and Barrow drove the team of three de Dietrich cars in the tragic Paris–Madrid race of 1903, and Barrow was one of the unfortunate drivers who lost his life in that catastrophic event. Travelling at 80 m.p.h. Barrow hit a dog which jammed his steering gear with the result that the big de Dietrich ran head-on into a tree beside the road and quite literally flew into small pieces. A combination of a large entry of very fast cars, and narrow, winding and dusty roads crowded with uncontrolled spectators had a most terrible result. The race was stopped at Bordeaux and proved to be the last of the great point to point road races. Henceforth racing was confined to a circuit where proper precautions could be taken. But besides tragedy the Paris–Madrid, or "The Race to Death" as the yellow press called it, was the occasion of what must surely stand as the most incredible motor-racing feat of all time. This was the performance of the winner, Gabriel, driving a 70 h.p. Mors. Starting 168th he drove through the scores of slower cars ahead of him, the blinding dust clouds and the wrecks to average the astounding speed of over 65 m.p.h. for the 340 miles.

Another very fine performance was that of Louis Renault driving a Renault of only 30 h.p. He won the Voiturette class and was second in the general classification with a speed of 63.2 m.p.h. While it is true that Renault started No. 3 and thus had a clear road, the performance of this comparatively small car (which had also won the Paris–Vienna race the previous year) was very significant and showed that the days of the giants were numbered. Their Waterloo was the French Grand Prix of 1912. Here the brains of the new overhead camshaft 7-litre Peugeot designed by Ernest Henri and driven by Georges Boillot proved more than a match for the brute force of the big Fiats of Nazarro, Wagner and Bruce Brown although their engines were nearly twice the cubic capacity of the Peugeot.

Though English drivers figured in these great events, except for the Napiers English cars played little part. In 1904 the Wolseley Company produced a team of three 96 h.p. cars for the Gordon-Bennett race. These had four-cylinder horizontally opposed engines and had a remarkably low centre of gravity for the period. Their unusual appearance earned them the nickname of the " Beetles ". Two Wolseleys, driven by Girling and Jarrott qualified in the Isle of Man eliminating trials and so represented England in the race itself at Homburg, where Jarrott finished twelfth. The cars were not entirely satisfactory and never scored any conspicuous success.

The opening of the Brooklands track removed one of the difficulties which had hitherto handicapped English racing car development by providing facilities for testing high-speed cars without fear of transgressing the law. Several designers were quick to take advantage of this facility, notably Louis Coatelen of Sunbeams and Laurence Pomeroy of the Vauxhall concern. Though not so advanced in their ideas as Ernest Henri, neither Coatelen nor Pomeroy pursued the cult of the large engine. On the contrary, the 2,000 miles trial of the R.A.C. in 1908 was divided into numerous classes on a basis of rated horsepower, and this encouraged English designers to search for more brake horse-power per litre instead of seeing how many litres of engine they could cram into a chassis. It was Pomeroy who realised what now seems obvious—that power output is dependent, not so much on engine size as on engine speed. At the same time better quality materials and improved methods of pressure lubrication made higher engine speeds possible and Pomeroy was able to build a small (by the standards of the time) and perfectly normal-looking four-cylinder side-valve engine of 3 litres which developed 17 b.h.p. per litre, or more than twice the average output at that date, simply because it ran up to 2,500 r.p.m. This car created a sensation in the R.A.C. trial. The same principle was followed by the Talbots and by Coatelen's Sunbeams both of which used higher speed side-valve engines, and it was triumphantly vindicated when the Sunbeams carried off first, second and third places in the French Coupe de l'Auto in 1912. This was run concurrently with the Grand Prix in which the Peugeot defeated the giants, and the little Sunbeams were also third, fourth and fifth in the general classification, thus securing the team prize. This was the first notable English victory on the Continent since Edge's Gordon Bennett win in 1902.

The Sunbeams taught the Continent a lesson, not only in what could be achieved by a small and relatively simple engine, but also in the value of streamlining. Experience on Brooklands had revealed the importance of reducing wind resistance, and whereas the continental racing cars were still square in outline with the conventional round bolster tank in the rear, in the Sunbeams frontal area was reduced to a minimum and the narrow body terminated in a stream-lined tail in which the tank was incorporated.

The Sunbeams and the Vauxhalls entered for the 1913 Coupe de l'Auto at Boulogne, but this time they encountered more formidable opposition in the shape of a team of three Peugeots fitted with 3-litre overhead camshaft engines designed by Ernest Henri on the lines of the larger Grand Prix cars. Although both the Sunbeam and the Vauxhall engines were producing a greater power output than before as a result of a higher compression ratio, larger

PLATE 19

(*above*) *The Napier team for the Gordon Bennett Cup,* 1903. *Drivers (left to right):
Stock, Jarrott and Edge ; (below) The Wolseley " Beetle " racing car of* 1904. *Bianchi
at the wheel.*

Courtesy A. S. Heal

PLATE 20

(above) The Coupe de l'Auto, Dieppe, June, 1912. Victor Rigal in the winning Sunbeam about to leave the pits. His mechanic : Jean Chassagne ; (below) Isle of Man T.T., June, 1914. A. J. Hancock, Vauxhall, comes over the mountain.

Courtesy A. S. Heal

valves and ports and lighter reciprocating parts, they proved
to be no match for the French cars. The Peugeots of Boillot
and Goux finished first and second with Guinness on the
Sunbeam third and Hancock, Vauxhall, fourth.

The lesson of this race was not lost upon either Coatelen
or Pomeroy. It showed them that there was a very definite
limit to the power output which could be obtained from an
orthodox side-valve engine unit, and that the future lay
with the overhead valve design which made possible better
combustion chamber and port design. The R.A.C. had
announced their intention of reviving the Tourist Trophy
race in the Isle of Man in 1914, and both Coatelen and
Pomeroy prepared new designs for this event. The Sunbeam was virtually a replica of the Peugeot, but Pomeroy's
T.T. Vauxhall displayed more originality. With twin shaft-
driven overhead camshafts and sixteen valves, fully counter-
balanced crankshaft and comparatively short stroke, the
Vauxhall was, in fact, an outstandingly advanced design.
Unfortunately, however, the racing history of the Vauxhall
firm resembles that of King Ethelred and the cars were not
ready in sufficient time before the race to enable the inevitable teething troubles to be overcome.

Two other English manufacturers, Straker-Squire and
Humber produced overhead valve engines for the race,
the Humber unit being designed by F. Burgess who was
later to collaborate in the production of the famous 3-
litre Bentley. The Tourist Trophy was won by K. Lee
Guinness on a Sunbeam, the sleeve-valve Minervas winning
the team prize by finishing second, third and fifth. This was
one of the very few successes achieved by sleeve valves in
racing. The Minervas were fitted with Knight double-
sleeves of the type used by Daimler. Smoothness and silence
rather than high performance were the outstanding qualities

of the Knight engine but adequate lubrication of the sleeve valves was only achieved at the cost of excessive consumption of the very light oil which had to be used, and the Minervas emitted a dense smoke screen which added considerably to the hazards of the race.

The last race of importance to be held before the outbreak of war was the 1914 Grand Prix de l'A.C.F. at Lyons and the design of many of the competing cars foreshadowed post-war practice. With the exception of certain sleeve-valve entries, overhead valves, generally driven by twin camshafts, reigned supreme. Ball, and in one case roller, main bearings were used instead of plain bearings by several designers. Moreover, for the first time in a Grand Prix, four-wheel brakes were used by Peugeot, Delage, F.I.A.T. and Picard-Pictet. England was represented once more by the Sunbeam and Vauxhall teams. These were enlarged versions of the 1914 T.T. cars, but as on the previous occasions the Vauxhalls suffered from the lack of timely preparation. The race was historic for two circumstances. Firstly, Mercedes returned to Grand Prix racing after a lapse of six years and finished first, second and third. Although superior in speed, this overwhelming victory of the German cars was due mainly to meticulous preparation and attention to detail and to the fact that for the first time in the history of motor-racing the running of the team was controlled by a team manager signalling from the pits, a practice universally adopted when racing was resumed after the war. Secondly, the Peugeots conclusively demonstrated to the motoring world the superiority of four-wheel braking, for although both the Mercedes and the Sunbeams proved superior in speed, more powerful brakes enabled the Peugeots to hold their own on the winding Lyons circuit. So much so that Boillot was able to hold first or second place until the penultimate lap when he retired with a broken valve, leaving his team-mate Goux to finish fourth ahead of the leading Sunbeam driven by Dario Resta.

The 1914 Grand Prix racing car was of only 4½ litres capacity, yet it was already superior in speed and in every other respect to the " giant racers " which met their Waterloo in 1912. Through the aegis of men such as Coatelen and Pomeroy, the influence of this rapid development on the evolution of the English car was very great.

Just as the Peugeots designed by Ernest Henri had dominated pre-war racing so, when racing was resumed after the war, it was the Henri designed 5-litre straight-eight Ballot which became the pattern of racing-car design. It is only fair to add, however, that Henri was undoubtedly influenced by Ettore Bugatti, and that it was a straight-eight Bugatti aero engine which prompted Henri to design the Ballot power unit. The pursuit of greater power output per litre resulted in the production of engines capable of turning over at revolutions which would have shocked pre-war designers. In this respect the straight-eight, with its lighter reciprocating parts, had the advantage of a four-cylinder engine of the same capacity, and consequently the former soon outnumbered the latter on the starting grid in Grand Prix events.

Of the English manufacturers, Louis Coatelen continued to pursue his policy of following Continental practice, and the 1921 3-litre Grand Prix Sunbeam was very similar in design to the Henri Ballot. Neither Sunbeam nor Ballot, however, achieved victory in the French Grand Prix which was revived in this year. The race was won by an American Duesenberg—the only occasion when an American car has won a classic Continental race. Once again Vauxhalls displayed more originality than

Sunbeams and designed a team of 3-litre cars with four-cylinder twin overhead camshaft engines designed by Ricardo which appeared in the Isle of Man T.T. race organised by the R.A.C. in 1922. A central flywheel was used in conjunction with a built-up crankshaft, the webs being shrunk on to the journals. Ball main bearings and roller big ends were fitted and the engine developed 129 b.h.p. at 4,500 r.p.m. Of all the racing essays of the Vauxhall concern this, their last appearance, was the most unfortunate and ill judged. As usual the cars were ill-prepared. The race was won by Chassagne driving a 1921 Grand Prix Sunbeam, Vauxhall only securing third place behind a Bentley with a tuned-up standard engine. The race was run under an obsolete formula because at the end of the 1921 season a Grand Prix formula limiting engine capacity to 2 litres had been laid down. Incredible though it may seem the Vauxhall Company never acquainted themselves with this fact and so, at great labour and expense, produced cars which were ineligible to compete in any other major event. Technical comparisons and subsequent history both reveal the tragedy of this extraordinary blunder, for the Vauxhalls were of remarkably advanced and efficient design ; so much so that had they been produced in 2-litre form England might have played a much more conspicuous part in Grand Prix racing in the 1920s. One of the 3-litre Vauxhalls, substantially in its original condition subsequently set up several class records on Brooklands, while another in supercharged form and somewhat misleadingly called the Villiers Supercharge, captured fastest time in many sprint events throughout the 1930s in the hands of Mays and Cummings.

One of the original features of the 3-litre Vauxhall was the use of Westinghouse air brakes, the only case within my knowledge of this well-known railway braking system being applied to a motor vehicle. Orthodox racing practice at this time was to assist the manual operation of the four-wheel brakes by means of a friction servo mounted behind the gearbox, and it was the American Duesenberg which first introduced hydraulic brakes to Europe.

In 1921 there had appeared a team of 3-litre straight-eight Fiats designed by a young Italian named Bertarione which marked the first radical departure from the accepted lines laid down by Ernest Henri. Steel cylinder blocks with sheet metal water jackets were used and not only the main bearings but the big ends were of roller type, the latter having split cages, thus obviating the necessity for a built-up crankshaft. Most important of all, Bertarione employed only two overhead valves per cylinder in place of the four used in the Henri designs. By doing so he secured a better gas flow, a better head shape, and space for more effective head cooling. These 3-litre cars were not conspicuously successful, but the scaled-down 2-litre cars which appeared in 1922 proved much more formidable by winning easily both the French Grand Prix at Strasbourg and the Italian Grand Prix at Monza. They thus showed themselves to be more than a match for the cars of Henri pattern.

As in 1913, so in 1922 Louis Coatelen was quick to appreciate the significance of the Italian success and he straightway captured Bertarione and bore him off to Wolverhampton. As a result the six-cylinder racing Sunbeams which emerged from that factory in the following year differed only in minor details from the 1922 Grand Prix Fiats.

In the 1923 French Grand Prix at Tours these Sunbeams were opposed by the new Fiats which differed from their predecessors in one most vital respect—they were fitted with superchargers. There have been several moments in the history of motor-racing when further major improvement seemed impossible. Then some revolutionary development has inaugurated a further cycle of growth. The racing car engine had attained such a pitch of performance in 1921–22 that it must have seemed to many contemporaries that only detail improvements were possible in the future. Already race organisers had become alarmed by the speed attained by the cars, and this was the main reason for the introduction of the Grand Prix formula limiting capacity to 2 litres. The fact that despite this restriction speeds continued to increase was almost entirely due to the revolutionary effect of the supercharger. It should be added, however, that the supercharger imposed greatly increased temperatures, pressures and stresses on the engine so that it was due to the combined efforts of chemist, metallurgist and designer that a high-pressure " boost " could be successfully applied. Thus although the supercharger is unlikely ever to be widely applied commercially, its use in racing has indirectly exerted a great influence on technical development, a fact which is forgotten by those who regard the modern racing car as a freak.

Perhaps it should be explained at this point that the ordinary internal combustion engine relies upon the suction of the piston on its downward stroke to draw into the cylinder from the carburettor an explosive mixture of air and petrol vapour. The amount of mixture drawn in by this means, or in other words the volumetric efficiency, is influenced by many factors. It is affected by the temperature of the mixture on admission, by the design of manifolds, ports and cylinder heads and by the lift and timing of the inlet valves. Careful design can therefore improve efficiency very considerably in this direction and this, to a great extent accounted for the success of the engine designs evolved by Henri and Bertarione. But the most meticulous designer could not overcome the fact that volumetric efficiency varied with engine speed, there being considerable loss of efficiency at both ends of the speed range. As engine speed steadily increased in the pursuit of greater power output per litre, the loss of efficiency at high speed became more and more apparent until the idea of forcing mixture into the cylinder by means of a compressor or " supercharger " was evolved.

The simple vane type compressor fitted to the 1923 Fiats was scarcely a supercharger in the modern sense of the word in that it did not deliver mixture under high pressure throughout the speed range but was designed solely with the object of maintaining efficiency at high revolutions. Like the Mercedes supercharger fitted at the same time, the Fiat unit delivered air at low pressure to the carburettor and did not, like the modern blower deliver compressed mixture drawn from a carburettor. Though they demonstrated their speed at Tours in a close fought battle with the Sunbeams, the new Fiats suffered various mechanical troubles, notably disintegration of the supercharger vanes, and the race was won by Segrave's Sunbeam, the first and only occasion when an English car and driver have won the French Grand Prix, the classic event on the Continental calendar.

When, two months later, the Fiats appeared at Monza for the Italian Grand Prix they were fitted with modern Rootes type superchargers delivering mixture under pressure throughout the speed range. This time their superiority was never in doubt. Two cars driven by Salamono and Nazarro finished first and second, five minutes ahead of their nearest rival. This was the first occasion on which a Grand Prix was won by a supercharged car, but so over-whelming was the advantage of this unit that, with the sole exception of the 1925 Targa Florio, no subsequent major event has ever been won by an " unblown " car.

It seems scarcely necessary to add that this lesson was not lost on Coatelen and that for the next season the Sunbeams appeared with Rootes superchargers. It is a measure of the advantage derived from forced induction that whereas the 1923 Sunbeam engine developed 108 b.h.p. at 5,500 r.p.m. the 1924 supercharged version, which was otherwise practically identical, produced 145 b.h.p. at 5,000 r.p.m., a gain of over 18 b.h.p. per litre. There seems to be little doubt that these Sunbeams were the fastest cars of the year, and only a cruel mischance robbed them of the distinction of winning the French Grand Prix for England for the second year in succession. On the eve of the race the magnetos were replaced by new Bosch instruments which, in the event, produced persistent misfiring sufficient to cost Sunbeams the race but the cause of which was not diagnosed until it was too late. The race was won by an Italian newcomer to Grand Prix racing but a name to conjure with thereafter—Alfa Romeo. England had her revenge later in the season, however, when the Sunbeam driven by Segrave won the Spanish Grand Prix at San Sebastian.

In 1925, the last year of the 2-litre formula, the Sunbeams were outclassed and two continental makes, Alfa Romeo and Delage, dominated the field. The fact that the twelve-cylinder Delage developed 190 b.h.p. at 7,000 r.p.m. which gave the car a maximum speed well in excess of 130 m.p.h. gives some idea of the progress made in the seven years which had elapsed since the end of the first world war. It also shows how completely the 2-litre formula failed in its object of reducing the speeds of the Grand Prix cars.

Nevertheless, the same object inspired the 1926–7 formula which restricted capacity to $1\frac{1}{2}$ litres.

With the close of the 1925 season, the name of Sunbeam, which had represented England on so many Continental circuits, disappeared forever from the annals of Grand Prix racing. Yet, so far as 1926 and 1927 were concerned, it was a disappearance confined to the name alone. For the Wolverhampton firm had become members of an Anglo-French Combine known as S.T.D. (Sunbeam-Talbot-Darracq) which constructed a series of $1\frac{1}{2}$-litre racing cars known variously and somewhat confusingly as Talbots, Darracqs or Talbot-Darracqs. For the sake of simplicity I propose to refer to them all as Talbots. The races for $1\frac{1}{2}$-litre cars which were held during the period 1920–25 were the equivalent of the voiturette races of pre-war years, and in these events the Talbots, which were really scaled-down editions of the current Grand Prix Sunbeams, performed with conspicuous success. The $1\frac{1}{2}$-litre Talbot which scored its first win at Le Mans in 1921 was a four-cylinder version of the Henri designed straight-eight Sunbeam of that year, and though challenged on occasion by Bugatti and Aston Martin, its victories became almost monotonous until 1924 when it was superseded by a Bertarione design.

So jealous were the S.T.D. directors for the reputation of these cars that when a team of supercharged Fiats which had shown a greater turn of speed than the Talbots were entered for the 200 miles race at Brooklands in 1923, they were unwilling to risk defeat and withdrew their entry. In the event their fears proved to be unfounded, for although the Fiats (one of which was driven by Malcolm Campbell) were the first $1\frac{1}{2}$-litre cars to lap the track at over 100 m.p.h. they retired with mechanical troubles and the race was won by a newcomer to racing, an Alvis driven by C. M. Harvey.

This car was a modified version of the famous 12/50 model which was introduced in that year, so that its winning speed of 93.29 m.p.h., 5 m.p.h. faster than the speed of the winning Talbot in the same event the previous year, was a surprising achievement.

The supercharged Bertarione Talbots proved as successful as their predecessors in 1924 and 1925, and neither the Aston Martin nor the straight-eight Alvis could match their performance, although the latter, with its front-wheel drive and independent suspension was a bold and in some ways advanced design. Nevertheless, when $1\frac{1}{2}$ litres became the Grand Prix formula for 1926, the S.T.D. group decided to introduce a new design. The resulting supercharged straight-eight Talbots were the last representatives of the marque to appear in International road racing. They were the swan-song of a concern which had consistently, and frequently alone, upheld the prestige of the English Motor Industry on the Continent ever since the Sunbeam victory in the Coupe de l'Auto in 1912. They were beautiful little cars which deserved success but failed to achieve it. Because, for the first time in 1926, the rule that Grand Prix cars must carry a mechanic was abolished, the designer of the Talbot was able, not only to reduce frontal area, but also to lower the centre of gravity of the car by offsetting the engine and transmission and so seating the driver beside, instead of above, the latter. Hitherto designers had only been able to reduce frontal area to a limited extent by cramming the unfortunate mechanic into a seat of the minimum dimensions which was staggered in relation to the driving seat in order to allow the driver elbow room. In these days when the single-seater racing car is ubiquitous the racing mechanician is a forgotten figure. As a highly nervous passenger I would pay tribute here to those gallant and unremembered men. Carrying his life in his own hands, the driver is too fully occupied to ponder the consequences of mishap or misjudgment once a race is in progress. The mechanic, on the other hand, had ample opportunity to envisage disasters which he was powerless to avert since he could do no more than place implicit faith in the dependability of car and driver.

Detail defects and faulty preparation repeatedly robbed the single seater Talbots of victory, nor did the other English aspirants, Aston Martin, Alvis and Thomas Special fare any better. This catalogue of defeats unfortunately included the only two International Grand Prix to be held in this country (at Brooklands) prior to the Silverstone race in 1949. Though inferior in performance to the Talbot, the reliability of the Bugatti not only brought the marque to victory at Brooklands in 1926 but also secured the Championship of Europe. In the following year Delage won these honours with consummate ease. This was scarcely surprising for the straight-eight Delage engine designed by Lory was an example of automobile craftsmanship which has rarely been equalled and never surpassed. It developed 170 b.h.p. at 8,000 r.p.m., a power output per litre which remained unequalled for a decade.

From 1927 until the end of the 1933 season a restrictive Grand Prix formula was abandoned and races were open to all comers. Racing history during these years, however, scarcely concerns us here. English cars did not compete in Continental Grand Prix, and these races ceased to play any important part in influencing the design of the English car. Instead, until 1931, interest turned to sports car racing which will be dealt with in another chapter. The main reason for this change of emphasis was that manufacturers both in England and abroad no longer considered the expense of constructing specialised racing cars each season to be justified. Consequently Ettore Bugatti, whose policy had always been to race what were virtually production cars, was left almost alone in the field until 1931 when the famous monoposto Alfa Romeo, and to a lesser extent the Maserati, put an end to the series of Bugatti victories and brought about a revival of interest in the genuine racing car.

In the 1½-litre Delage of 1927, the history of motor racing reached another static phase when further major development seemed impossible. So far as engine design is concerned this is still substantially true today. But despite enormously increased power output, chassis design had not changed to a comparable degree. Apart from the introduction of frontwheel brakes in 1914, chassis development had been merely a story of refinement and detail improvement. With immensely powerful brakes, low centre of gravity and perfect weight distribution, a car such as the monoposto Alfa Romeo represented the ultimate that could be achieved within a convention which dated from the earliest days of motor-racing. Yet such was the power developed that the road-holding ability of the chassis had become the decisive limiting factor on a road circuit.

In one important respect the racing car of the '20s and early '30s was at a disadvantage compared with the chain driven monsters of the first decade of motor-racing. With their narrow tyres, countershaft differentials and sketchy rear wheel braking systems, unsprung weight on the early racing cars was reduced to the minimum and it was largely due to this that they were able, despite flimsy chassis, high centre of gravity and bad weight distribution, to perform such prodigious feats. The introduction of live rear axles, larger tyres and increasingly powerful four-wheel braking systems resulted in a great addition of unsprung weight. Moreover, this increase was accompanied by a progressive decrease in sprung weight in proportion both to unsprung weight and to the power and speed developed. On any wheeled vehicle the purpose of springs is to absorb the shocks which the wheels and axles receive as they pass over an uneven surface and which they would otherwise transmit to the frame of the vehicle. Provided the weight of the vehicle is substantially greater than that of the wheels and axles, the the springs will exercise this damping effect with reasonable efficiency. Moreover, by holding the wheels to the road despite inequalities, a good factor of adhesion will be maintained. But it will be apparent even to the non-technically minded that if the excess of sprung to unsprung weight is substantially reduced a point will be reached when, as one writer has very aptly expressed it " the tail begins to wag the dog " ; in other words the springs will no longer be capable of damping the forces generated by road shocks in the wheels and axles. The latter will therefore tend to take charge and destroy the stability and road-holding capacity of the vehicle. Moreover, where a solid axle beam is used, a road shock received by one wheel cannot, in any event, be completely absorbed and damped out by the contiguous spring but is partially transmitted through the beam to effect the opposite road wheel and to set up, via the springs, complex stresses and strains in the frame.

As the racing car developed, designers were forced to pay an increasing amount of attention to this problem although, until 1934, their answers took the form of a crude though surprisingly successful form of compromise rather than a true engineering solution. From the first, no attempt was made to resist the stresses transmitted to the frame through the springs by trying to evolve a completely rigid chassis. Instead a flexible chassis frame was made capable of withstanding these stresses by absorbing them. In effect, therefore, the chassis itself became an additional damping device. In the early cars this principle was carried to great lengths, and it was to prevent engine and gearbox castings from damage as a result of this flexing that the practice of mounting these units in a sub-frame was almost universal. Later, chassis became stiffer, particularly at the front end, when it became necessary to meet the new stresses imposed by front-wheel braking, but a certain degree of flexibility was always maintained; indeed good road-holding depended on this quality when spring movement was restricted.

The increasing tendency for unsprung weight to take charge of the car was countered by assisting and controlling the springs by means of more powerful shock absorbers of friction or hydraulic type. Considering the crudity of its principle, the friction shock absorber was a remarkably successful device. It consists merely of an adjustable disc brake interposed between the axle and the frame, its cardinal fault being that its positive damping effect is not adaptable to road shocks of varying strength and periodicity. Consequently, though the use of friction shock absorbers brought about a great improvement in road-holding, the most careful adjustment could only secure the best results with a given load at a particular speed. For example, friction shock-absorbers tightened to give the necessary control at maximum speed will often so nullify the effect of the springs at slower speeds that the car becomes virtually unsprung thus causing poor adhesion, discomfort to passengers and submitting the chassis to added strains. It was with the idea of overcoming this disadvantage that, in the 1930s, a type of friction shock absorber was introduced which could be adjusted from the driving seat.

The principle of the hydraulic shock absorber, whereby the damping effect is derived from the compression of a liquid, is obviously more efficient and adaptable to changing conditions than that of the friction disc. In practice, however, a really efficient hydraulic shock absorber is a large, complicated and costly piece of mechanism as compared with a friction shock absorber of equivalent capacity. Consequently, although the De Ram hydraulic shock absorbers which were fitted to certain racing cars, including E.R.A.s in the 1930s were probably the most efficient spring damping device ever designed, the small hydraulic units fitted to production cars at this time were of practically no value, and the great majority of sports cars continued to rely on friction dampers.

At a very early date Morgan in England, Sizaire Naudin in France and Lancia in Italy had introduced the principle of independent suspension on the front wheels of their cars. In 1926 the Alvis joined this select company with their independently sprung front wheel drive car which also demonstrated the fact that driven wheels could be treated in the same way. Yet it does not appear that even these few manufacturers who utilised independent suspension ever fully grasped its potential advantages. It was left to Germany to demonstrate to the world the overwhelming advantages of independent wheel springing through the performance of their Mercedes and Auto-Union cars in Grand Prix racing between 1934 and 1939.

This, the second re-entry of Germany into the lists of Grand Prix racing was as carefully prepared, as spectacular and as successful as their first sensational reappearance in the 1914 French Grand Prix. Although initially the Mercedes, and to a greater extent the less conventional rear-engined Auto-Unions, suffered from teething troubles which at first enabled the hitherto invincible Alfa Romeo to meet their challenge, it was immediately evident that the static phase represented by the latter was over and that a fresh era of development had begun.

For 1934 a Grand Prix formula limiting the weight of cars to 15 cwt. had been introduced with the same purpose of reducing power and speed as the 1,000 kilo formula of 1902. Like its predecessor, this formula completely failed to have the desired effect, the German cars developing unprecedented power per kilo of weight, although power per litre showed no great advance on the 1927 Delage. The secret of their success was the use of independent suspension which enabled such power to be fully and safely utilised in a car so light in weight. The elimination of the rigid axle beams which had hitherto increased unsprung weight and transmitted shocks and strains enabled the old canons of design to be reversed, a rigid chassis being combined with flexible springing. It was sufficient to watch the German cars in action to realise that the result was road-holding and control of an order hitherto undreamed of. I still vividly recall the astonishment with which I watched the Mercedes and Auto-Unions travelling down the narrow and bumpy straight at Donnington at speeds in the neighbourhood of 150 m.p.h. The difference between their gait and that of the cars with orthodox suspension resembled that between an ambling palfrey and a trotting horse. Whereas considerable wheel movement was apparent to the eye, the German cars remained perfectly steady, the drivers sitting as still and as relaxed as the passengers in a railway carriage. The other cars, by contrast, might have been judged to possess no springs at all as they bounded along, their drivers bouncing uncontrollably. This eloquent object lesson which the German Grand Prix cars provided

Courtesy A. S. Heal

PLATE 21

(*above*) *The* 1922 *Isle of Man T.T.* : *The* 3-*litre Vauxhall driven by O. Payne,*
which finished third, on Ramsey hairpin ; (*below*) *Dario Resta at the wheel of the* 1924
2-*litre G.P. Sunbeam.*

Courtesy A. S. Heal

PLATE 22

(*above*) The 1926 *supercharged straight-eight Talbot* ; (*below*) The first E.R.A., 1934.

PLATE 23

(*above*) "*Shelsley Special*" : *John Bolster's* "*Bloody Mary*" *ascends Prescott ;*
(*below*) *The* "*500 Special*" : *Colin Strang at Prescott.*

PLATE 24

THE EVOLUTION OF A CLASSIC SPORTS CAR

(*above*) The " *Prince Henry* " *Vauxhall*, 1910 ; (*below*) 1921 *E type* 30/98 *Vauxhall
with Velox body.*

has initiated a revolution in automobile engineering design in England and elsewhere which, interrupted for a time by the second world war, is still in progress. That the principle of independent suspension when applied to the cheap mass-produced car does not necessarily lead to such happy results is a matter irrelevant in this chapter.

Although English cars, as distinguished from English drivers, played no part in Grand Prix racing during the 1930s, the prestige of the English industry was most worthily upheld by the E.R.A. which performed with conspicuous success in innumerable 1½-litre events both at home and abroad. To a lesser extent the racing M.G. " Magnette " and " Midget," the Alta and the amazing little single-seater Austin " Sevens " demonstrated what prodigious power British designers could conjure from engines which would have been looked upon as toys in the days of the " giant racers."

The E.R.A. is remarkable as the only racing car sufficiently successful to be called a classic type which has been evolved from a standard production touring car and not designed throughout for racing. Its basis, as has already been mentioned, was the Riley, and the lion's share of the credit for this, the most successful English racing car since the great days of the Sunbeams, is due to Raymond Mays who performed the potent transformation in his workshops at Bourne. The parent of the E.R.A. was the famous " White Riley " with which Mays astonished the motoring public by establishing a new record at Shelsley Walsh in 1933.

The introduction of a 1½-litre (supercharged) formula for post-war events has enabled England, with her E.R.A.s, to compete once again in full scale Grand Prix racing. These cars, the majority of which were built well before the war, have performed most creditably. Latterly, however, they have not been able to match the speed of the new Italian cars and, like the Bugattis in 1926, they have had to depend for success upon superior reliability. It is to be hoped that the new British racing car which enthusiasts so eagerly await will prove itself both as fast and as reliable as the invincible Talbots of the early '20s.

Little or no reference has so far been made to track racing on Brooklands or to world's land speed record attempts in in which latter sphere England has always been pre-eminent. Neither subject needs detailed consideration in a chapter designed primarily to illustrate the influence of the racing car on the general development of design. In both track racing and flying start record breaking where a high maximum speed is the main consideration, the problem of reducing wind resistance becomes all important, and the development of streamlined forms has probably been their most important contribution to the sum of technical knowledge. In March 1926, Segrave raised the world's speed record to 152.33 m.p.h. driving a twelve-cylinder super-charged Sunbeam of 4 litres capacity on Southport sands. Since then, astonishing though the achievement has been, the record has been the province of specialised machines fitted with enormous engines of aircraft type whose design, apart from their streamlined form, has had little influence on automobile engineering development.

It is the Grand Prix road race that has always been, and is likely to remain the supreme testing ground and stimulant of development. Consequently the Grand Prix car is always the embodiment of advanced design allied to the highest standard of engineering craftsmanship. The fault of Grand Prix racing from the purely sporting point of view is that the cost of running, let alone producing, a modern Grand

Prix car has passed far beyond the means of the individual, while even manufacturers hesitate to compete as they have done in the past. The development of the pre-war German cars was subsidised by the State to advertise Nazi supremacy. However tempting the prospect of a subsidy may appear to the enterprising designer it were better, in my view, for the sport of international road racing to die out altogether than that it should degenerate into a series of gladiatorial combats grimly fought between rival State teams seeking to win, not for sport, prize money or even commercial prestige but as instruments of political propaganda. Such a prospect would disgust the men who drove the giants long ago. Adventurers of Elizabethan quality, they drove for the love of the game and their spirit still lives on at those peculiarly English events, the sprint meetings and speed hill climbs organised by such bodies as the Midland Automobile Club, the Bugatti Owners' Club or the Vintage Sports Car Club. Here the driver of the costly racing car finds himself challenged, and occasionally worsted, by some home-made " special " built in a country garage or back-yard workshop.

The study of the English sprint " special " is a fascinating one and it is fitting that a recent book, wholly devoted to the subject, should have been written by Mr. John Bolster one of the most enterprising builders and certainly the most spectacular driver of these individual racing cars. The great majority of the earlier specials proclaimed in their unashamed nakedness that they possessed a common ancestor in the G.N. cycle-car. Their performance was frequently remarkable, but like their common prototype their success appeared to be due more to good luck, courage and unbounded optimism than to technical achievement. Spidery specials of this variety may still be seen, but in recent years their numbers have been leavened by an infinite variety of hybrids, some of which exhibit advanced features and a standard of workmanship which bears comparison with the pure racing car. Then, too, there has been the astonishing rise to popularity since the war of the small special powered by a 500 cc. motor-cycle engine, a popularity so great as to justify the commercial production of a car of this type.

The home-made special is the product of months, perhaps years, of painstaking labour, of trial and error often fraught with bitter disappointment and frustration. But when at last the troubles are overcome and the car really shows its form the builder-driver can appreciate better than any other racing driver how Charles Jarrott must have felt as he crossed the finishing line in his crippled Panhard in the Paris–Vienna race so long ago.

CHAPTER EIGHT

THE SPORTS CAR

THE TITLE OF this chapter requires some preliminary definition. To some people the term sports car suggests a cross between a touring and a racing car intended primarily for competition work, while to others it implies a vulgar, noisy or otherwise ostentatious vehicle designed to appeal to wealthy and irresponsible young men. Examples can be found to justify both these definitions. On the one hand there is the racing car adapted for road use or the freak trials car with sketchy bodywork and enormous knobbly tyres ; on the other there is the pseudo sports car in which a special body, and perhaps an inefficient silencing system disguise an engine and chassis of mass-produced mediocrity. Neither of these types will be mentioned in this chapter.

The appeal of the true sports car is to those who do not merely regard the motor-car as a convenient method of travelling from place to place but who take pleasure in the art of driving and in the car itself as a piece of engineering craftsmanship. It must therefore possess a very high standard of performance, and by performance is meant not only powers of acceleration and maximum speed but superlative road-holding and cornering qualities, truly progressive braking and accurate steering. Moreover, all the controls should possess a quality of robustness combined with precision and delicacy of movement which can alone ensure that the car responds instantly and exactly to the requirements of the driver. A car which possesses these qualities is a delight both to own and to drive. It at once demands, encourages and rewards the exercise of skill on the part of the driver. It is pertinent here to remark that although the age of mass production has produced cars equalling or even excelling many true sports cars in speed or acceleration, it has not yet, in my estimation, succeeded in reproducing on the assembly line that subtle combination of qualities which characterises the thoroughbred. Good road manners and accurate steering, in fact, are qualities which have never yet been cheaply produced. The fact that so many mass-produced cars are not only designed to be driven with the minimum of skill but are capable of speed far in excess of their roadworthiness is probably the greatest single cause of the tragic increase in road accidents in recent years. This, and the complementary fact that, other conditions being equal, the quality sports car is a far safer vehicle than the average modern touring car, is very seldom appreciated.

I do not believe that the specific term " sports car " became current until after the first world war. In the earliest days when motoring was an adventure and every motorist was a sportsman it would be equally true to say that there were no sports cars or that every vehicle justified the use of the term. Here, however, the sporting element lay in uncertainty of behaviour rather than distinctive quality so that driving was as much a battle of wits against mechanical vagaries as an exercise of skill. Later, when the motor-car took definitive form and until the first world war, the quality of construction, of steering, road-holding and braking was, within the limits of technical evolution, generally high and widely diffused throughout the industry. Consequently, when there emerged from the ranks what we now recognise as the ancestors of the classic sports cars of the 1920s, they were known as "fast touring cars" and were distinguished from their more staid contemporaries solely by a superiority in speed which they derived from increased engine efficiency combined with a good power-to-weight ratio. It was not until the period between the wars when pursuit of the goals of quantity and cheapness led to a progressive eclipse of quality in the motor industry that the term sports car was evolved and came to mean, among discerning motorists, much more than superiority in speed alone. The sports car thus became the exemplar of qualitative standards of design which, apart from specialised racing cars on the one hand and a few high-priced luxury touring cars on the other, would otherwise have been lost.

To survey the cars of the Edwardian era and to select from them the ancestor of the sports car is a somewhat invidious task. Yet I am inclined to share Mr. Cecil Clutton's opinion, expressed in his writings upon this subject, that the 4-litre " Prince Henry " Vauxhall has the best claim to be the prototype. This was the production equivalent of the 3-litre Pomeroy designed car which, as related in the last chapter, caused such a sensation on its appearance in the R.A.C. 2,000 miles trial of 1908, and whose secret lay in the high speed of the otherwise normal side-valve engine unit. The 4½-litre side-valve Talbot closely followed the lines laid down by the " Prince Henry," and it was one of these cars which, driven by Percy Lambert on Brooklands in 1913, was the first to cover over a hundred miles in the hour.

As we have seen, the side-valve engine in racing cars was very soon superseded by overhead-valve units of the type evolved by Ernest Henri. Yet it was some years before the superior potentiality of the Henri design was developed to an extent sufficient to justify its application to a production "fast touring car." Increased complication and expense coupled with a probable loss of reliability, though justifiable in the design of a racing car, were rightly held to outweigh any slight gain in performance. Hence the fact that the "Prince Henry" Vauxhall design held the field in England until 1922. In 1913, an enlarged version of the "Prince Henry," with a bore and stroke of 98 mm. × 150 mm. which gave a capacity of 4½ litres, was produced for the express purpose of setting up a new record at the Shelsley Walsh hill climb. This car not only achieved its immediate object, but showed such remarkable capabilities that it was put into regular production. In this way there was born a model which many regard as the most famous and historic sports car of all time—the "30/98" Vauxhall. In 1923 this original model, the E type as it was called, was succeeded by a type known as the OE. This had push-rod operated overhead valves but was otherwise basically similar and should be considered as a development rather than a radical change. It can therefore be said that a fundamentally Edwardian design continued until 1928 when production of the OE 30/98 ceased.

To study the comparative performance of these two models of the same car is to obtain an interesting insight into the changing standards of the pre-war and post-war epochs. Though their performance is of a very different and more refined quality, a comparison between a "Silver Ghost" and a "Phantom I" Rolls Royce gives a somewhat similar result. The overhead-valve version of the 30/98 possessed a greater power output than the side-valve type, while engine revolutions were higher, the stroke was shorter, and the final drive ratio was accordingly lowered. Moreover, the OE type offered opportunities for further tuning which the E type did not, and as a result the former has performed with distinction in speed events down to the present day. The chief characteristic of the older car was the amount of power developed at low engine speed, and this combined with the light weight of the car to produce fast and effortless cruising in the high top gear of 3 : 1. The OE Vauxhall was a magnificent machine and was unquestionably more potent than the older car, yet, having driven both, my personal preference is for the latter. The OE, with its less flexible engine, not only called for a more judicious use of the gears if it was to give of its best but, in the process of giving that best it always seemed to convey the fact that it was hurrying, by what I can only describe as a general impression of mechanical commotion. This impression was lacking on the side-valve car whose engine rumbled along sweetly and happily at any gait from 20 to 80 m.p.h. and there can be no doubt that it fulfilled more fully the original description of " a fast touring car." The cardinal fault of both cars was that their stopping abilities were by no means commensurate with their speed. It is true that the rear wheel brakes of the older cars were little inferior to their contemporaries, but this cannot be said of the four-wheel brakes fitted to the OE type. On the latter, direct operated brakes of inadequate size and stopping power were succeeded, on the last cars, by a hydraulic system of Vauxhall's own design operating on front wheels and transmission. Although the front brake drums were of most impressive size, in practice they could but rarely be induced to act in concert, if at all. Consequently the older system with its known limitations was preferable to one in which each application of the brakes might produce a totally different and disconcerting result. Because of this failing, special braking systems were evolved for those

Vauxhalls which performed with most success in competition in the late '20s and '30s.

It was not until after the first great war that an English sports car appeared which embodied the Henri overhead camshaft technique. This was the famous 3-litre Bentley. Actually the car may be said to have combined current French and German practice since it was the fruit of a collaboration between Burgess (who had designed the 1914 T.T. Humber on Henri lines) and W.O. Bentley who had raced a D.F.P. before the war. By comparison with the E Type Vauxhall engine which developed 98 h.p. at 2,500 r.p.m. the standard "red label" Bentley produced about 86 h.p. at 3,500 r.p.m. But whereas it was virtually impossible to coax any more horses from the former, the Bentley engine was capable of considerable development as is shown by the claim that the 3-litre engines fitted to the Le Mans cars produced well over 90 h.p. at 3,500 r.p.m. Owing to the high stroke to bore ratio (80 × 149) piston speed was high by contemporary standards, but the power developed at low speed was poor and good performance called for full use of the four-speed close ratio gearbox. Unlike the Vauxhall, the Bentley was equipped with four-wheel brakes of ample size and reasonable efficiency but paid the penalty in increased unsprung weight. Although on the first experimental car which appeared in 1919 the total weight was kept down, the standard 3-litre weighed 27–28 cwt., a figure which compares very ill with the E type Vauxhall which weighed 22 cwt. complete with its Velox aluminium panelled four-seater body. This illustrates the besetting fault of the manufacturers during the decade 1920–1930 which in all other respects may be called the Golden Age of the English Sports Car. Although the importance of a favourable power/weight ratio was as clearly appreciated by Pomeroy as by Dr. Darwin in 1765, it seems to have been either forgotten or ignored by his successors. Time and again we find an admirable design burdened by progressively heavier components and coachwork, until it would almost seem that their makers vied with each other in seeing, not how well their respective cars could perform, but which could bear the heaviest millstone.

The 3-litre Bentley and its successors the 4½-litre (subsequently supercharged) and the Speed Six rank with the Vauxhall as classic sports cars and contributed more than any other make towards the prestige of the English industry by their successes in sports car races. The modern Bentley with its developed version of the Rolls Royce 25 h.p. engine is a fine car with a performance worthy of both the names with which it is associated ; but it perpetuates the Bentley tradition in name only. That tradition was built up by W. O. Bentley and the men who drove his cars : by Sir Henry Birkin, Doctor Benjafield, S. C. H. Davis, Jack and Clive Dunfee, Woolf Barnato, Jack Barclay, Glen Kidston and E. R. Hall, and it is with their names that it will always be linked. It was the performance of the Bentleys in the hands of these men in events both at home and abroad, and particularly in the Le Mans twenty-four hour race, that so enhanced the reputation of the English sports car during the temporary eclipse of Grand Prix racing. In fact it was largely due to their efforts that our success in this field was very much greater than anything we have so far achieved with specialised racing cars.

One of these Bentley achievements is worthy to rank beside Gabriel's drive in the Paris-Madrid as one of the epics of motor racing. This was the victory of the " Old Number Seven " 3-litre Bentley driven by S. C. H. Davis and Doctor Benjafield at Le Mans in 1927. The best account of this dramatic race was written by Davis himself in his book *Motor Racing*. The whole of the Bentley team (which included a " $4\frac{1}{2}$ " appearing at Le Mans for the first time) became involved, through no fault of their own, in a sensational multiple crash at a point on the course known as White House Corner. This disaster happened in darkness and at a time when the Bentleys, headed by Clement and Callingham in the " $4\frac{1}{2}$," were comfortably leading the race. Less damaged than the other cars, " Old Number Seven " was extricated from the wreckage and, in a desperate attempt to mitigate the disaster, was driven on. With a bent chassis and front axle which affected both the steering and the brakes it must indeed have seemed unlikely that the car could possibly last for the twenty-four hours. But as time went on the driver's confidence in the abilities of the crippled car returned, and its speed increased until the possibility of the car securing a place became almost a certainty. Finally came the dramatic moment, only an hour before the finish, when the leading car, an Aries driven by Chassagne, stopped by the roadside with engine trouble and the battered Bentley swept past to victory.

Owing to the increasing burden of taxation the Vauxhalls and Bentleys virtually held a class monopoly in England during the 1920s as manufacturers concentrated to an increasing extent on sports cars with a capacity of 2 litres, $1\frac{1}{2}$ litres and, later, 750 cc. The only notable exceptions which spring to mind were the $4\frac{1}{2}$-litre Meadows engined Invicta (often called, on account of its low build, the " flat iron "), the 3-litre Sunbeam and the " 105 " Talbot. Every sports car worthy of the name attracts a certain following of devoted enthusiasts with the result that comparisons are inevitably odious. Nevertheless I dare to express the opinion that the " 105 " Talbot was probably the best all-round sports car of this trio. Although it was a very fast and attractive car, the Invicta was occasionally subject to expensive mechanical explosions. Also a centre of gravity unusually low for the period encouraged the driver to take liberties on corners, which were not always justified by results. As ultra-low-built cars with orthodox suspension are apt to do, it seldom gave warning, in the guise of a controllable skid, of the fact that the limit of control had been reached. Thus although it might be capable of rounding a given corner at a greater speed than a car with a higher centre of gravity, if that speed were exceeded the car would fly off the road in a four-wheel slide.

The overhead camshaft engine of the 3-litre Sunbeam was a beautiful piece of engineering based on that of the 2-litre Grand Prix racing Sunbeam, and had the chassis equalled the capabilities of the engine it might have achieved greater popularity and success. As it was, an unusually long wheelbase combined with a comparatively narrow track made the Sunbeam difficult to control especially on wet roads.

With his 1910 " Type 13 " and post-war " Type 23 " (the famous " Brescia "), Ettore Bugatti has an almost unassailable claim to be called the father of the small high-efficiency sports car. In England before the 1914 war, though there were a number of light cars with qualities which might be called sporting, the type cannot be said to have existed, but its origin and development after the war was due not so much to the example of Bugatti as to the influence of Brooklands track racing in general and the 200 miles race organised by the Junior Car Club in particular. In this event the aspiring light car manufacturers of the post-war boom period vied with each other keenly, and the majority of the first 1½-litre sports cars to appear on the

English roads were versions, more or less detuned and modified, of 200 miles race cars. Characteristics which they nearly all shared were a very light two-seater body of polished aluminium panelling and a very vocal exhaust system. The latter frequently took the form of a large external pipe curving round the body side. The record in this respect was set up by the " Speed Model " Hillman (also one of the first cars of the type to appear) which flaunted a burnished copper external pipe of stovepipe dimensions which was guaranteed to attract an awed group of admiring small boys wherever the car came to rest. Unless it was more or less forcibly dissuaded by the unfortunate driver, the curiosity of this audience invariably led to burnt fingers. Connected to this imposing piece of coppersmith's work was a perfectly normal side-valve engine. Nevertheless, thanks to its light weight, the car possessed quite a good performance with a maximum of 65 m.p.h., while a special 1½-litre Hillman called *Mercury* set up an hour record for its class at 78.23 m.p.h.

One of the most popular and certainly the fastest 1½-litre sports car to appear in the early '20s was the Frazer-Nash. This was a direct development of the G.N. cycle-car which, as we have seen, was the product of a partnership between H. R. Godfrey and Captain A. Frazer Nash. Besides their " popular " model, which was described in a previous chapter, G. N. Ltd. produced a successful twin-cylinder sports car known as the Vitesse. The Company also scored many successes in competition with the twin-cylinder racing cars *Kim*, *Akela* and *Mowgli*. The last named formed the basis of B. H. Davenport's famous *Spider* which for many years held the record at Shelsley Walsh hill climb. But in 1922, as a result, it is said, of commercial competition from the Rover " 8," G. N. Ltd. suddenly decided, not only to drop the twin engine in favour of a four-cylinder unit, but to abandon their unique form of chain transmission for an orthodox drive. This latter decision evidently failed to please Captain Frazer Nash for he left the firm and proceeded to build, under his own name, what was virtually a G.N. chassis only slightly modified and fitted with a four-cylinder engine. Events proved him right. The shaft-driven G. N. proved a commercial failure. In 1924 the Company re-adopted chain drive using the Anzani engine but they were too late, for the Frazer Nash had already captured the market.

The prototype Frazer Nash was fitted with an overhead valve engine known as the " Powerplus " but this was soon dropped in favour of the side-valve Anzani and it was in this guise that the car became famous. Fitted with a very light aluminium body, the Anzani Nash combined the peculiar charm and the almost fortuitous handling qualities of the G.N. cycle-cars with an outstanding performance. Although its sketchy and uncomfortable coachwork combined with a certain crudity which it inherited from its predecessor made the Nash essentially an enthusiast's car, it was undoubtedly one of the most outstanding sports cars ever built. Its unique qualities were worthily perpetuated in later examples of the marque which were fitted with Meadows or Blackburne engines, although with added weight and complication, some of the charm of the original was lost.

The Anzani Nash, in common with other contemporary side-valve cars such as the 12/40 Alvis might be described as miniature editions of the E type 30/98 Vauxhall. Like the latter they possessed the virtue of good power output at low engine speeds but they were not capable of much further development. Thus although the Anzani Nash was more than a match for its more advanced contemporaries, it was doomed to extinction, as the potency of the latter was developed. The ultimate development of the Anzani Nash was the application of a Cozette supercharger in which form the engine developed about 80 b.h.p. and gave the car a maximum speed of 95 m.p.h. But this was achieved at the cost of transforming a hitherto reliable engine into a potential source of dire mechanical disintegration.

Meanwhile the 12/40 Alvis underwent a precisely similar transformation to that of the E type Vauxhall with equally successful results. A new cylinder block and head having push-rod operated overhead valves was fitted to the 12/40 crankcase and thus the celebrated and long-lived 12/50 Alvis was born. The performance of the special Alvis in the 1923 200 miles race has already been mentioned. In standard production form the car was inferior in maximum speed and acceleration to the Frazer Nash, but the chassis was a beautiful example of English automobile engineering at its best and consequently the car was capable of sustaining its very creditable performance with complete reliability for many years. The aluminium bodied two-seater sports 12/50 with 1½-litre engine weighed 17½ cwt. and was capable of a speed of 75–80 m.p.h. It was a pity that this model was dropped in favour of an engine of longer stroke the cubic capacity of which slightly exceeded 1½ litres. Also that as the years went by the willing engine was handicapped by progressively heavier chassis and bodies. Its final form as a sports car was the 12/60 " beetle-back " two-seater of 1931. The use of dual carburettors and enlarged valve ports had increased the power output from 50 to 60 b.h.p. at 4,500 r.p.m. but the car weighed 25 cwt. Part of this increase over the original model was admittedly due to the addition of front-wheel brakes and a stiffer chassis

PLATE 25

TWO FAMOUS SPORTS CAR PROTOTYPES

(above) 1923 12/50 *h.p. Alvis with two-seater body by Grose ; (below)* 1925 *Frazer Nash with s.v. Anzani engine.*

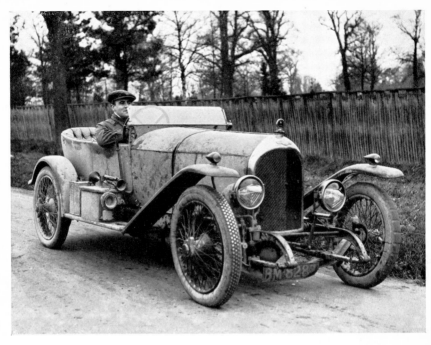

PLATE 26

(above) The first experimental 3-litre Bentley with Captain W. O. Bentley at the wheel, January, 1920 ; (below) The sports car in closed form : The Talbot " 105."

PLATE 27
UPHOLDERS OF THE QUALITATIVE TRADITION IN THE '30s.
(*above*) The *Aston Martin* " *Ulster* " *model ;* (*below*) *The first production model* H.R.G., 1935.

PLATE 28

POST-WAR TRANSFORMATION

(above) The 1939 Rover 10 *saloon ; (below)* The 1950 Rover " 75."

frame, but the car reflected no attempt to save weight. The steel panelled body was inordinately heavy without even offering any commensurate advantage in improved comfort or roominess. Thus the increased output of the engine was largely occupied in propelling additional weight with the result that the performance showed little or no improvement over that of its 8-year-old predecessor. As already stated, this was an all too common story in the history of the sports car during the late '20s and early '30s.

In 1928 there appeared a production version of the front-wheel drive Alvis racing car which was briefly mentioned in the previous chapter. The four-cylinder engine was very similar to the 12/50 except for the fact that its valves were operated by an overhead camshaft. It developed 50 b.h.p., or 75 b.h.p. in supercharged form. In the following year it was succeeded by a 1½-litre straight eight of similar basic design which in stripped, supercharged form was sold with a guaranteed maximum of 100 m.p.h. These cars were certainly fine performers and ran with distinction in sports car races, notably in Ulster and at Le Mans, but as a commercial proposition they proved too costly to produce. The front-wheel drive called for a somewhat different handling technique, but once this was mastered the car was well mannered except for the fact that, under certain circumstances it was handicapped by lack of front-wheel adhesion. I can well recall one wet day at Shelsley Walsh when Frank Hallam's Alvis almost came to a standstill on the steep section between the corners owing to wheel spin. Historically the interest of these cars lies in their pioneer use of independent suspension on all four wheels. This was affected by transverse quarter elliptic leaf springs. Four of these springs controlled each front wheel and adjustable clips over the leaves took the place of shock absorbers. Moreover the unsprung weight of the front wheels was reduced to a minimum by mounting the front brake drums on either side of the final drive casing. This is a principle which we may well see re-adopted now that unsprung weight reduction is receiving serious attention. On the Alvis, however, it was subject to the grave disadvantage that the removal of the front brake shoes for relining was a major operation.

Following the 12/50, and discounting the front-wheel drive experiment, the Alvis Company produced a number of different models of progressively larger size beginning with the 2-litre six-cylinder " Silver Eagle " and culminating with a car of 4.3 litres capacity. Though all these cars were characterised by an unusually high standard of workmanship at a time when qualitative standards were declining in the industry, and although they were fine performers, it has never seemed to me that they entirely fulfilled the promise of the 12/50 largely owing to their unnecessarily high weight.

Two other sports cars which earned an enviable reputation during the period between the wars were the Aston Martin and the Lagonda. The former originated in a hybrid " special " with which Lionel Martin performed with success at Aston Clinton hill climb, and it was in this way that the name of the car originated. The first production car appeared in 1921 and, like so many of its contemporaries, it was powered by a 1½-litre side-valve engine. In October of that year Kensington-Moir demonstrated its abilities by covering 86.21 miles in the hour. This proved to be the first of a long series of record achievements and sports car racing successes at Le Mans and elsewhere. Despite the undoubted success of their early cars, the Aston Martin concern were one of the first to drop the side-valve unit, jump the push-rod compromise, and produce a sixteen-valve overhead camshaft engine directly based on the Henri designed 3-litre Ballot. Subsequently, though very few sixteen-valve cars were made and engine design has varied according to the ideas of Benson, Renwick and Bertelli, Aston Martin have always maintained the overhead camshaft principle. The production Aston Martins were probably the most handsome-looking sports cars ever built in England, nor was their quality confined to their looks. On the contrary they combined excellent road manners with a performance which was only marred (it must be repeated yet again) by excessive weight. Two detail criticisms which may be advanced against them were, firstly, poor mechanical accessibility on the later cars and secondly that the " cycle type " front wings attached to the brake back-plates, though neat in appearance, added unnecessarily to unsprung weight.

The history of the Lagonda Company began before the first world war with a three-wheeler and a successful 12 h.p. light car, but it was the 2-litre model introduced in 1927 which securely established the reputation of the firm. The engine of the 2-litre was a four-cylinder with twin overhead camshafts which were driven, together with the auxiliaries, by a very long roller chain which, in its convolutions round various sprockets, was reminiscent of certain agricultural implements. However, I have always been biased in favour of gear driven camshafts whatever their position, and there can be no doubt that the Lagonda engine was a reliable and efficient unit. Despite the use of fabric bodies, the complete car was unusually large and heavy for its engine capacity and this made it rather sluggish. An alternative model was fitted with a low-pressure supercharger which made good this deficiency. A fault of the early Lagondas was a serious chassis weakness, the main side frame members having a tendency to fracture at a point a little distance aft of the rear engine bearers. This defect was remedied in a somewhat crude fashion by introducing a truss of similar pattern to those fitted to eight-wheeled railway carriages. The 2-litre was succeeded by push-rod overhead-valve four and six-cylinder cars, by the short-lived 1½-litre " Rapier " model and by a 4½-litre model which, in its special " Rapide " form, performed with conspicuous success. Finally there appeared the big vee twelve-cylinder car designed by W. O. Bentley which featured independent front suspension by torsion bars. Two cars of this type finished third and fourth at Le Mans in 1939.

Other sports cars of the between-war years which merit mention were the sports versions of the 2-litre A.C., the Riley (particularly the " Brooklands' model of the latter) and the Lea Francis. The Lea Francis with its 1½-litre push-rod overhead-valve engine was introduced in 1925 and was very similar in character and performance to the 12/50 Alvis although it did not quite equal the latter for reliability and longevity. In 1927 the firm caused a sensation by marketing a somewhat similar model fitted with a Cozette super-charger, and this was quickly followed by the celebrated " Hyper-Sports " car. This last was an extremely fast though somewhat explosive machine, and its most notable success was its hard-won victory over the front-drive Alvis team in the 1928 Ulster Tourist Trophy race.

The growing demand for a sports car of miniature pro-portions was catered for largely by a sports version of the Austin Seven and by the M. G. " midget." Though never remarkable for good road-holding and steering, the former ably demonstrated the amazing amount of power which could be produced from a diminutive side-valve engine. The ultimate in this respect was achieved by the first series of special supercharged single-seater Austin racing cars. Though I have no figures available I should guess that these cars developed the greatest power output per litre ever achieved from a side-valve engine. By contrast with the Austin, the M.G. employed an overhead camshaft engine which represented the ultimate development of the old Wolseley 10 engine mentioned in a previous chapter. M.G.s scored innumerable successes in competition, the most potent sports and racing models being the " Montlery " the independently sprung " R " type, and the larger " Magnette."

So far we have only considered the better known examples of what has become known as the " vintage " era of English sports car design. There were many other worthy marques which failed to survive the decade. Two of these vanished sports cars, the Beardmore and the Arrol-Aster, came from Scotland which has never been a fortunate country for the automobile industry. Like the A.C. concern, Beardmores made extensive use of light alloys at an early date. They produced two models, a 14/40 h.p. side-valve car and a 2-litre overhead camshaft super-sports model. A racing version of this car scored a number of successes in the hands of Cyril Paul including the fastest time of the day at Shelsley Walsh in 1924. The Arrol-Aster, as its name denotes, was the product of the amalgamated firms of Arrol-Johnston Ltd., and the Aster Engineering Company. Two models with six and eight cylinders were produced and both, like the other Scottish car the Argyll, were fitted with sleeve valves. Though their performance was scarcely meteoric they acquitted themselves well in the Alpine trial in 1929.

Two English makes which did not deserve to perish were the Straker-Squire and the H.E. The former had been a

name to conjure with before 1914 when the 15 h.p. cars
held a number of class records and were very successful in
hill-climbs.   The larger 20/25 h.p. six-cylinder Straker-
Squire was known, like the 30/98 Vauxhall, as a "fast
touring car" and, thanks to a chassis weight of only 17 cwt.,
it had the same capacity for effortless high-speed cruising on
a high back-axle ratio.   The H. E. (Herbert Engineering
Company) emerged during the post-war boom.   Although
the first 14/40 h.p. model had a four-cylinder side-valve
engine of somewhat archaic appearance, its performance
was little inferior to that of the contemporary 3-litre
Bentley in its standard form.   Moreover, with their flared
wings, narrow bodies and Bugatti-like radiators, the two
and four-seater H.E.s were rakish, handsome-looking cars
in their day.   At the end of the '20s the Herbert Engineering
Company produced a six-cylinder car which was more
sober in appearance and behaviour, but this proved to be
their swan-song.   The Company were notable for unusual
ideas about suspension.   Their first cars, like the early Aston
Martins, used three-quarter elliptic rear springs, while when
front-wheel brakes were fitted a unique arrangement of
reversed quarter-elliptic front springs appeared.   These
resembled semi-elliptic springs, but the portion between
axle and front dumb-iron was solid.

Another vanished make which favoured unusual suspension was the Horstmann.   Both the production sports
models and the special 200 miles race cars were fitted with
side-valve Anzani engines and cantilever springing all
round. Having driven one of the latter I can testify that the
unorthodox springing was a complete success, road-holding
being conspicuously good.   The weight of the complete car
was only 9¾ cwt., an achievement which was reflected in
performance.   The Horstmann was distinguished in two

other respects ; for being the first English car to fit a supercharger (in 1923) and for fitting a kick starter in the driving compartment of their standard models.

A number of fine Continental importations helped to swell the ranks of the fast cars to be seen on the English roads towards the end of the '20s. From France came Bugattis of various types, the " DISS " Delage with its mahogany decked " boat " body, the two-litre Ballot and, in the smaller class, Amilcar, Salmson and Senechal. From Italy came the " 22/90 " Alfa Romeo, first of a succession of fast cars from this famous factory ; the independently sprung Lancia " Lambda " ; the Diatto and the O.M. which, like the H.E., continued to champion side-valves. Germany's most notable representatives in England were a succession of progressively larger Mercedes culminating in that supreme example of Teutonic brute force the 38/250 h.p. supercharged " SSK " Mercedes-Benz. This last is the only car in which I have driven at a speed exceeding three figures on an English road under normal conditions. Even though a car may be mechanically capable of 100 m.p.h. the magic figure is by no means so easily attained on the road as the layman might suppose from motorists' tap-room talk which, like that of anglers, is apt to be coloured by alcohol and imagination.

In 1930/31 the golden period of sports car production in England came to an end. The financial slump at once reduced the demand for individually built cars and favoured the introduction of mass production methods. A few makers, most notably Aston Martin and Frazer Nash, continued to uphold the qualitative tradition well into the '30s but many more began, to a greater or lesser degree, to exhibit those sad symptoms of the triumph of quantity over quality which we noticed in Chapter 6. Only one new

English car appeared in the 1930s which qualifies for a mention in this chapter. This was the H.R.G. and it is significant that the " G " in these initials stands for Godfrey of G.N. fame. Although shaft-driven in an orthodox manner, the appearance of the car, with its quarter-elliptic front springs carrying the front axle well forward of the radiator, unmistakably revealed its ancestry. Altogether the clean and workmanlike lines of the H.R.G. were a refreshing sight at a time when bonnets were protruding over front axles and dropsical bulges of useless sheet metal were everywhere becoming more apparent. There was nothing revolutionary about the H.R.G. ; it was simply a straightforward and well-built car in the best tradition of the past decade. Its most notable characteristic was the fact that for the first time since the early '20s it was evident that the importance of a good power/weight ratio was fully appreciated by the designer. The car weighed only 14 cwt. and this enabled the 1½-litre Meadows engine, which developed 58 b.h.p. at 4,500 r.p.m. to give the car a very fine performance.

The sensational advent of the independently sprung German Grand Prix Cars has forced even the most ardent devotee to admit that the classic sports car of the 1920s was at last destined to become obsolete. Such a revolutionary improvement in chassis design could not fail to have an equally profound effect on the development of the English car. There is inevitably a time-lag in the application of racing car developments to the production vehicle, and before the lesson of the German cars could be fully assimilated the second world war intervened. Consequently it is only within the past two years that English cars have appeared which embody the fruits of pre-war racing experience.

It would, I consider, be invidious and undesirable in this book to mention current models by name and discuss their respective merits and demerits. I will therefore confine myself, in my last chapter, to a general consideration of the modern trend in design as it affects not only the sports but the touring car. Such a comprehensive view is made easier by the fact that, for good or ill, there is unlikely ever again to be so clear a distinction between the two types as there was in the " vintage era " between 1920 and 1930.

CHAPTER NINE

PRESENT AND FUTURE PROSPECTS

BY THE TIME the second world war broke out in 1939, motor manufacturers in this country and on the Continent had, with one significant exception, all accepted to a greater or lesser extent the American principle of mass production. The exception was to be found, not in England but in France and his name was Ettore Bugatti. Like Sir Henry Royce, Ettore Bugatti was pre-eminently a craftsman who never deviated from that qualitative standard which alone can determine the right relationship between the man and the machine. Because he knew the limitations of the latter his methods were a complete inversion of the practice of his contemporaries, many of whom regarded him as an eccentric. His production methods were to simplify machine operations so far as was practicable and to rely upon skilled hand fitting. The fruits of this heretical policy will be obvious to anyone who has lifted the bonnet of a Bugatti. Though it may be hard to imagine John Ruskin or William Morris becoming enthusiastic Bugatti owners, those stalwart champions of human dignity would have found little to cavil at in Bugatti's works at Molsheim. With the recent death of Ettore Bugatti, quality lost its last champion and the motor industry in Europe one of its most illustrious figures. In England a flourishing Bugatti Owners' Club reveals that the significance of his achievement has not been lost.

There is a small minority which, like myself, believes that

modern highly mechanised production methods can never match the qualitative achievements of Sir Henry Royce or Ettore Bugatti ; that the flexible mountings and other modern devices which cloak inferior workmanship can be no substitute for innate excellence. There are many more to argue that modern methods have been so perfected that there is no product of the craftsman which they could not faithfully reproduce. I doubt this. But even if an attempt were to be made to mass-produce a replica of a " Silver Ghost " Rolls-Royce or a 57s Bugatti, the cost of " tooling up " such a plant would prove so prohibitive that the demonstration would defeat its own object by proving instead the superiority of the craftsman over the machine.

Though it may be said that a mass-produced car must always lack that elusive quality which characterises the product of the craftsman, it would be wrong to declare that a reasonably efficient car cannot be produced by modern methods or that the inferior products of the 1930–39 era were wholly and irrevocably the result of those methods. On the contrary a great deal depends upon the degree of control which is exercised over production and upon those responsible for that control. As we have seen, the dominance of the Production Engineer and the Salesman over the Designer were in part responsible for the inferiority of pre-war mass-produced cars. An encouraging step towards grace which is apparent at the present time is the return of the skilled designer to his old position of pre-eminence. The result has been a marked improvement in general behaviour, if not in materials, appearance and finish, of the post-war car compared with its predecessor of the '30s.

The greatest single source of this improvement has been the successful application of the principle of independent suspension. Some years before the war there had appeared on the English market a mass-produced car with independently sprung front wheels, but the design followed American and not Continental practice, profiting not at all from the example set by the German Grand Prix cars. In fact little more can be said for the American system as it was exemplified at this time than that it was a sales-promoting gadget. American sales and advertising departments came nearer to the truth than they realised when they christened their new system " knee action." For the action of the front wheels was indeed apt to resemble that sagging at the knees, that strange lack of physical co-ordination which afflicts those who have imbibed well but unwisely. Although Chesterton's " rolling English drunkard " may have been responsible for the rolling English roads they were certainly unsuited to mechanical instability of this sort. Front wheels were all too independent in their action, and with this extreme flexibility was allied a complete failure to grasp the fact that independent wheel springing was not merely a new gadget to be hung on to the chassis. On the contrary its successful application involves the careful re-distribution of weight away from the centre of the car, a rigid chassis and, above all, a low centre of gravity. These canons are the opposite of those which characterised the classic sports car of the 1920's with orthodox suspension where weight was concentrated towards the centre of chassis, which was often very flexible, and where the centre of gravity was often high. Post-war designers have learnt this lesson and have shown that where it is faithfully put into practice flexible springing, within prescribed limits, is compatible with road-holding abilities hitherto unequalled. But unless wheel movement is kept within limits and unless the whole layout is most carefully designed, the geometry of the front wheels will be affected by their movement and this defect was particularly noticeable in the case of the early American system. This despite the pioneer examples of Morgan and Lancia whose coil spring systems proved entirely satisfactory.

Post-war systems of independent suspension generally fall into two groups. One employs coil springs in a somewhat similar fashion to the American suspension except for the important difference that the linkage ensures proper geometry. In the other system the wheels are mounted on links connected to the chassis by means of a rod of special steel known as a " torsion bar." In this case the springing effect is derived from the twisting moment imparted to the bar by the links. Thanks to the efforts of the metallurgist who has produced a steel capable of absorbing this moment without fatigue indefinitely, the torsion bar system has proved most successful. In both coil spring and torsion bar systems the links may be either parallel or trailing (i.e., fore-and-aft). In the former layout two torsion bars are placed along the chassis members, while the latter arrangement employs a single transverse torsion bar. But it may well be that in the next few years we shall witness the gradual supersession of steel springs in any form by hydraulic or even pneumatic systems of independent suspension.

The long overdue abolition of the system of taxation based on rated horse-power has encouraged a change in engine design which represents a sensible compromise between the extremes of the " buzz-box," producing its power only at high revolutions, and of the flexible but rough long stroke engine characteristic of the early classic sports cars. Upon this basis engine units have been produced which combine efficiency almost equalling that of a racing car with hitherto unprecedented silence and docility. Moreover, the importance of a good power to weight ratio has never been so clearly recognised since the early 1920s. What happens when a highly efficient modern engine unit is combined with low over-all weight and a sound system of suspension was conclusively demonstrated recently when an English production sports car recorded a timed speed of 134 m.p.h. Though some may argue that such a speed is neither necessary nor desirable in a road car, of the technical achievement which it represents there can be no question. Nor is this welcome improvement by any means confined to sports or high-priced cars. The current Morris Minor is a good example of a small, low-priced mass-produced car which is totally different from and in every way superior to, its pre-war equivalent.

To the layman who neither knows nor cares by what method the wheels are attached to the chassis or what makes them revolve, the most notable change in the modern car is the revolution in its appearance which has been brought about by streamlining. The proud radiator of the '20s which became a sham façade of sheet metal in the '30s has now, in many cases, vanished altogether from sight. It seems subtly symbolic of this machine-dominated age of ours that the motor-car, which began life as a friendly, characterful and highly individual machine has now grown into a formidable and inhuman-looking monster, distinguishable from its fellows only in detail. Headlamps no longer appear as lamps but as eyes that glitter in menacing fashion from the form of which they have now become an integral part. Between them a whale-like snout protrudes above the mouth through which the creature draws its air. In American cars this mouth bears a fixed and fatuous chromium-plated grin reminiscent of a popular toothpaste advertisement, but current Continental practice favours an orifice of smaller and strictly functional design. This gives the car a much more formidable expression reminiscent of the puckered mouths of those symbolic figures which, on old maps, whistle up the winds. At the time of writing, English design appears to be wavering between these extremes of which the latter is at least more honest.

It is not possible for me to accord to streamlining the praise which has been given to other aspects of post-war automobile design in England. In many cases (though not in all) it represents merely the logical development of that process already described whereby the motor-car became ashamed of the poverty of its mass-produced nakedness and proceeded to clothe its anatomy in sheet metal. Sales jargon about the virtues of streamlining have proved an effective method of educating the public to accept a motor-car that is wholly swathed in tin. Efficient streamlining is not merely important but vital in the case of aircraft or record-breaking cars, but it is by no means established that the principle affords any measurable advantage at any speed normally attained on the road. Certainly the experiments made on the railways before the war with streamlined locomotives reached the conclusion that any slight advantage gained was not sufficient to warrant the adoption of streamlining.

Probably the only valid advantage of streamlining as applied to the average car is that smooth unbroken surfaces are easier to clean, but even this advantage must be set against reduced accessibility and the added cost of making good the damage resulting from a minor accident due to " one piece " construction. Certain higher quality cars, however, demonstrate that by good design streamlining can be combined with accessibility, though in such cases the cost of streamlining probably exceeds that of normal bodywork so that the question of its justification crops up once more.

Whether or not streamlining can be technically justified, it seems clear that because the salesmen and advertising agents have now educated the public to accept the cult, production considerations will alone be strong enough to ensure that a race of whale-like monsters will in future monopolise the roads of England. But it is to be hoped that for a few more years at least a few manufacturers will continue to cater for that old-fashioned minority who, like myself, prefer a car which is not merely unashamed of its component parts but proud to display their fitness, excellence of design, workmanship, and finish.

If we look further than the immediate future we must consider the possibility that the piston engine may be eventually superseded by some other form of prime mover. Already there is talk of gas turbines or the possible use of atomic energy, while the dream of using electric vehicles which would pick up " broadcasted " electric power might one day come within the bounds of possibility. But, to take the longest view, we should not forget that so soon as man ceased to depend solely upon the strength of men and beasts aided by wind and water power, but invoked the powers of steam and internal combustion, he ceased to live on income but began to consume at an ever-increasing rate the capital resources of his planet. Therefore, if we assume that man acquires sufficient wisdom to avoid some atomic disaster, it becomes easy to imagine the time when the inhabitants of a denuded earth will regard with amazed incredulity the way in which this age of ours squandered its limited supplies of fuel. Although we might harness the winds and waters to electric generators on an unprecedented scale, these powers could never equal the

PLATE 29

(*above*) *The modern sports car : The* 1950 " XK120 " *Jaguar ; (below) The modern luxury car : Daimler straight-eight with drop-head coupé body by Hooper.*

immense amount we consume today in the shape of coal and oil.

When we survey the changes which the age of internal combustion has wrought in England it is not difficult to sympathise with those who wish that the motor-car had never been invented. Thousands of acres of once productive land have been lost beneath a desert of concrete and tarmac ; swollen cities have sent their sprawling tentacles far into the countryside ; the village community, that most precious unit of English life, disintegrates rapidly as road transport sucks its life and autonomy away ; only a few remote corners of our island are now immune from the roar and fume of the internal combustion engine, and all the while the road claims its toll of injury and death.

We may well consider this development tragic, but to single out the motor-car as the villainous scape-goat of the tragedy is to admit our failure to get to grips with the problems of the modern world and to concede that the machine has become the master of the man. It would be fairer to say that technical development, of which the motor-car is but one manifestation, has outrun our wisdom. This, in turn, is due to the fact that since the eighteenth century we have regarded scientific progress as an end in itself. Consequently " the man in the street " whether he be poet, philosopher or politician pursues in vain the headlong flight of the scientist and the engineer. No sooner does he imagine that he is at last gaining ground than he trips over some new epoch-making discovery that has been lightly tossed in his path by the leaders, and by the time he has recovered himself they are as far away as ever. The pace has become increasingly hot and he is steadily losing the race, but unless the rôles of pursuer and pursued can be exchanged the future outlook is dark indeed.

One result of this headlong technical progress has been that the potential value of past conquests has been squandered in the reckless and ill-judged pursuit of new achievements. This is evident on the English roads today. Despite the fact that petrol supplies to the private motorist have been limited, the traffic on many of our main roads is as dense as it was in the unrationed days before the war. Now petrol rationing has ended, the result in many cases may be chaotic, and for this reason plans are being made to deface and destroy still more of the English countryside with bleak multi-track highways. Yet every motorist will confirm from his own observation that the cause of the present congestion is a vast increase in the volume of commercial road transport since before the war. Day and night a procession of heavy goods vehicles thunders along our trunk roads damaging road surfaces, bridges, and the fabric of roadside buildings, disturbing sleep, consuming vast quantities of precious fuel and obstructing all other traffic. Yet all the while those other and older trade routes, our canals and railways, which are so much better fitted to carry goods traffic, have been allowed to become wasting assets. In the interests of fuel economy alone, any sane economy would develop these assets, leaving our roads free for passenger traffic and short-distance goods distribution. For such a function our present roads are perfectly adequate and the costly (in the real as well as the financial sense) schemes for new trunk roads would not be necessary.

As for the sprawling suburb and the week-end bungalow, they represent a civilisation that has lost the art of living either in towns or in the country and which, by attempting to combine some of the advantages of each, has succeeded in destroying the life of both. To admit that the modern suburb could not exist without the aid of the motor-car, and its big brother the bus, is not the same thing as to say that they are responsible for the suburb. The true source of the suburb is to be found in that industrialism which has fouled our cities and large towns and which has imposed on the majority an intolerable monotony of employment in surroundings either hideous or soul-destroying. The natural reaction of the individual to such conditions is to seek to to escape from them as far as his means will permit so soon as his working day is done, and for this purpose the internal combustion engine has proved to be the most convenient form of magic carpet. It is a sobering thought to reflect that every working day a most prodigious amount of irreplaceable fuel is expended upon the task of conveying millions of people millions of miles to and from their work, and that every day this mileage is increasing. Until Industrial Revolution becomes Industrial Devolution by a resolve to subordinate technocracy to human needs and human welfare, no amount of planning (that current cure-all) can materially alter this state of affairs. Meanwhile let us not look upon our willing steed the motor-car as an evil mechanical genius because we have made it the handmaid of chaos. The motor-car is simply a machine designed to transport us simply, quickly and efficiently from one place to another. Because it makes use of the road and is not confined to the waterway or to the steel rail it links your doorstep directly with mine. It should therefore promote human understanding and good neighbourliness within this small island of ours. If it has not done so ; if instead we have misused it in frantic and fruitless efforts to escape from the environment we have created, the fault lies not in our machines but in ourselves.

BIBLIOGRAPHY

The following were the principal works consulted in the preparation of this book. They are placed in chronological order.

The Lives of Boulton and Watt by Samuel Smiles, 1865.

Richard Trevithick (Memorial Volume) by H. W. Dickinson and A. Titley, 1934.

Steam on Common Roads, by A. Fletcher, 1891.

Steam Engine Builders of Norfolk, by R. H. Clark, 1948.

The World on Wheels, by H. O. Duncan (Paris) 1926.

Ten Years of Motors and Motor Racing, by Charles Jarrott, 1906.

The Motor Year Book, Methuen, 1905.

The Life of Sir Henry Royce, by Sir Max Pemberton, n.d.

Rolls Royce Memories, by Massac Buist, privately printed 1926.

" Racing Car Evolution ", 1895–1933, by Messrs. Clutton, Heal, Pomeroy and Scafe, *Motor Sport* March, 1942, Sept.–Nov., 1942, March, April 1943.

Motor Racing, by S. C. H. Davis, n.d.

British Sports Cars, by Gregor Grant, 1947.

"The Evolution of the Sports Car ", 1908–1938, by C. Clutton, *Motor Sport,* June, 1944.

The Magic of a Name, by Harold Nockolds, 1947.

Brooklands (3 vols.), by W. Boddy, 1948.

INDEX

INDEX

INDEX

INDEX

INDEX